D0385509

INDUSTRIAL CREATIVITY

the psychology of the inventor

INDUSTRIAL CREATIVITY

the psychology of the inventor

JOSEPH
ROSSMAN

INTRODUCTION BY GARDNER MURPHY

UNIVERSITY BOOKS  *New Hyde Park, New York*

Library of Congress Catalog No. 64-16161
Manufactured in the United States of America

DEDICATED TO
KNOWN AND UNKNOWN INVENTORS
WHO TOIL FOR HUMANITY

INTRODUCTION

IN THIS ERA of rapidly increasing interest in the problem of human creativeness, and of new experimental and clinical methods of adding to our biographical understanding of men of genius, I very heartily welcome the appearance of Joseph Rossman's work, *Industrial Creativity: The Psychology of the Inventor,* and congratulate the publishers upon this imaginative step taken to meet a public need.

Rossman's book came to my attention when it first appeared over thirty years ago. I was impressed with the author's very rich experience in working with inventions and with his obvious sophistication in the use of historical and psychological source materials. I was also delighted by the charm and vigor of his style. I have always referred students to Rossman's work with the feeling that here was something really vital and important. The fact that most psychologists did not latch on to my suggestion did not discourage me, for it has been my experience that "lay" or non-psychological writers are rather slow to gain adequate response from professional psychologists. Rossman, moreover, talking about inventors rather than about poets or about composers, would not reach the large public which exists for the expressions of creativity in the artistic-aesthetic areas of life. It was unfortunate that so important a book should fail to reach its adequate public at the time of its appearance—all the more exciting and noteworthy that this masterful collection of carefully documented material with intelligent and well balanced analysis and critique should now be made available to the general reader. The book is even more timely than it was when it was published. It will add to our understanding of those men who stand on the bridge between pure science and pure application in the daily tasks of the engineer or applied scientist. It will do more: it will add to our understanding of the basic psychology of creativeness. We still do not know enough about the raw, primitive quality of the creative act, and there is a great deal of material that we most need on this process contained here within this volume. I am sure that the reader will read both with great pleasure and with great gratitude for his increasing understanding of the fundamental human capacity to create.

GARDNER MURPHY

Menninger Clinic
Topeka, Kansas
December, 1963

AUTHOR'S INTRODUCTION TO THE PRESENT EDITION

IN MY ORIGINAL PREFACE I stated: "As an innovator and leader, the inventor performs one of the most important functions in society, for he holds the key to further progress." During the thirty years since my book appeared, the amazing technological progress has been brought about by a new type of inventor who might be designated as the scientist-inventor, that is, a creative individual who is thoroughly familiar with the latest scientific discoveries in his specialized field and who applies such discoveries to practical uses. The atomic reactor, for example, was patented by Enrico Fermi and Leo Szilard, the transistor was patented by Bardeen, Brattain and Shockley, the cyclotron by Dr. Ernest O. Lawrence, streptomycin by Dr. Selman A. Waksman, the Polaroid camera by Dr. Edwin H. Land, plutonium separation by Dr. Glenn T. Seaborg, nylon by Wallace H. Carothers, the optical maser by Dr. Arthur L. Schawlow and Dr. Charles H. Tunnes, the artificial kidney by Dr. Willem J. Kolff, the solar battery by G. L. Pearson, D. M. Chapin and C. S. Fuller, Teflon by Roy J. Plunkett, organo metal catalysts by Karl Ziegler, isotactic polymers by Giulio Natta, the synthesis of one of the B-complex vitamins by Roger J. Williams, synthetic fibers by Gaetano F. D'Alelio, geodesic dome structures by Richard B. Fuller, the apparatus for determining partial oxygen pressures by Linus C. Pauling, etc., etc. Certainly these outstanding scientists have not tarnished their intellectual respectability because they made practical applications of their scientific discoveries which inured to the common good. Hundreds of similar recent advances in technology are direct applications of scientific discoveries. In many instances the scientific discovery and its direct application for practical purposes have been made by the same individual. In other words, more scientists are today applying and searching for useful and practical applications of their discoveries. The National Science Foundation reports that in 1962 there were 339,400 full-time scientists and engineers in American industry. The aircraft and missiles industry employed 105,200 R & D* scientists or 31% of the total employed by industry. The electrical equipment and communication industry employed 75,300, the chemicals and allied products industry 35,300, and the machinery industry 32,300. These R & D persons in one way or another are engaged in creating new knowledge and new technology at a tremendously increased pace that will revolutionize and change our lives in many unforeseen ways even beyond the vivid imagination of our science fiction writers.

The dollar volume of industrial R & D performance more than tripled during the 10-year period from 1953 to 1962, increasing from $3.6 billion to $11.6 billion. A major reason behind this growth in industrial R & D activities was the increasing dollar volume of federally sponsored research and development contracted to private industry. In 1962, federally financed industrial R & D performance totaled $6.7 billion, over four and one-half times the corresponding amount of $1.4 billion for 1953. During the 1953-62 period, the federally financed portion of industrial R & D performance increased from 39 to 58 percent. The tremendous increase of federally sponsored research in recent years indicates that the advancement of science and technology is one of our important national objectives, not only for defense purposes but also for increasing our standards of living. Actually, such objectives are written into our federal Constitution which states in Article 1, Sec. 8, that "The Congress shall have the power...To promote the progress of science and

*Research and Development

useful arts, by securing for limited times to authors and inventors the exclusive rights to their respective writings and discoveries." The Atomic Energy Acts of 1946 and 1954, and the National Aeronautics and Space Act of 1958 have resulted in state control of technical information on inventions in specific new fields of technology which are of military importance. Just what effect such control will have on private incentives to invent in these fields is to be seen.

Scientific and technological advances are made by creative individuals. In spite of the huge research organizations which have been developed by private industry, by non-profit organizations, or by the federal government, the key to new discoveries and inventions is the creative brain of an individual. Teams of scientists and technicians are useful in accelerating the development and application of new ideas, but only a creative individual can spark the flashes of creative idea. John Jewkes in his book, *The Sources of Inventions* (1958) made a study of the inventorship of 61 important recent inventions. He found that 33 were made by individuals working on their own, 21 were made by company-employee inventors and the rest were of mixed technological parentage. He concludes that we need not despair of the survival of the individual inventor because he is still making startling and important contributions. He also believes that the large highly organized industrial laboratory does not appear to be a particularly favorable environment for inducing invention. Also "the inventor who becomes part of an organization cannot expect to be wholly immune to the traditional frustrations." He concludes further that "the large research organizations of industrial corporations have not been responsible in the past fifty years for the greater part of the significant inventions. These organizations continue to rely heavily upon other sources of original thinking."

I am myself convinced that it is more important than ever to explore and understand the psychological basis of creativity. We will then be able to stimulate and develop creativity in all human activity and thus carry our civilization to great achievements not only in our physical environment but also in our social and spiritual lives.

In re-reading my book at this date and in the light of my

professional experiences as practicing patent attorney for the past 25 years, I feel that most of the objective data regarding the inventor which I presented are still valid today. I have met professionally a very large number of inventors and have had the opportunity to discuss with them the circumstances and the events which led to the development of their inventions. Their experiences appear to confirm the statements made in my book. In fact, I am disappointed not to be able to report any startling departures from the inventors' techniques as reported in my book. However, what is most gratifying is the recent increased psychological research being carried on in regard to creativity. Professor J. P. Guilford of the University of Southern California, for example, reported that of some 121,000 titles which appear in *Psychological Abstracts* from 1927 to 1960 he found only 186 titles which definitely bore on the subject of creativity. Since then there has been a marked increase in research projects in the field of creative imagination. The Creative Education Foundation of the University of Buffalo, in a "Compendium of Research on Creative Imagination" (1958), listed 30 research studies concerned with the identification and development of creative ability. The second compendium published in 1960 reported 27 additional published studies and 26 current research projects. In 1955 the Industrial Research Institute published a "Bibliography on Creativity" which lists 1,919 items. In 1961 the U.S. Naval Research Laboratory published an annotated bibliography by Mildred Benton, "Creativity in Research and Invention in the Physical Sciences," which lists 1,359 items. This bibliography constitutes an excellent supplement to the original bibliography of my book. In addition, the recent book, *Creativity and Innovation* (1962) by John W. Haeffele, a research chemist at Proctor and Gamble Co., contains an excellent survey of the recent literature relating to deliberate creativeness. He lists 187 significant literature references. His book in many ways supplements and brings this book up to date. Other useful references deserve mention: E. L. Hutchinson, *Materials for the Study of Creative Thinking,* 28 Psych. Bull. pages 392-410 (1931) which lists 152 references; W. Platt, *The Relation of the Scientific 'Hunch' to Research,* 8 J. of Chem. Educ. 1969-2002 (1931); Morris I. Stein and Shirley J. Heinz, *Creativity and the Individ-*

ual (1960), summarizes selected pertinent literature, including the present book; *Creativity and Its Cultivation,* edited by Harold H. Anderson (1959) presents views of 15 students on various aspects of creativity; *The Creative Process,* edited by Brewster Ghiselin (1952) contains statements by 38 authors; S. J. Parnes and H. E. Harding, *A Source Book of Creative Thinking,* (1962); Eugene K. Von Fange, *Professional Creativity* (1959); Calvin W. Taylor and Frank Barron, ed. *Scientific Creativity: Its Recognition and Development,* (1963) contains selected papers presented at the 1955, 1957 and 1959 National Conferences at University of Utah; Catherine Patrick, *What Is Creative Thinking* (1955) includes a bibliography of 210 references. S. E. Golann, *Psychological Study of Creativity,* Psych. Bull., Vol. 60, Nov. 1963, pages 548-565, reviews recent literature relating to theories of creativity and viewpoints of investigators.

It is interesting to observe that in 1952 Congress enacted a new patent act, Title 35, which contains essentially the same provisions as the previous law except that a new Section 103 was added in an attempt to define an objective legal test for determining when an invention is patentable. It reads:

> "A patent may not be obtained... if the differences between the subject matter sought to be patented and the prior art are such that the subject matter as a whole would have been obvious at the time the invention was made to a person having ordinary skill in the art to which said subject matter pertains. Patentability shall not be negatived by the manner in which the invention was made."

It is evident that trying to determine whether an invention is "obvious" in the light of objective facts which existed prior to the date when an invention is conceived requires making a judgment which is highly subjective and which is influenced by the personal experiences, technical education and emotional set of the judge. The last sentence in the Section 103 quoted above admonishes the judge to ignore any facts relating to the "manner in which the invention was made." This sentence deserves some historical comment. In 1941 the U.S. Supreme Court in the case of Cuno Eng. Corp. v. Automatic Devices by Justice Douglas stated that only inventions made by a flash of creative genius are patentable. This pronouncement raised a storm of criticism from inventors and patent attorneys as not being an objective or realistic test; Congress paid heed and provided the quoted last sentence of Section 103.

It has been suggested recently by some economists that the tremendous increase of research and development expenditures in recent years also should have increased the output of patented inventions. The number of patent applications filed in recent fiscal years and patents granted is shown in the following Table:

Fiscal	Number of U.S. Patent Applications Filed	Number of Patents Granted	Percent of Patents Granted
1962	84,864	51,065	60.2
1961	80,842	47,222	58.4
1960	78,995	50,322	63.8
1959	77,978	52,184	67.0
1958	76,565	43,407	56.7

A comparison of this table with Table 14 on page 178 of my book shows that the number of patent applications being filed annually has declined rather than increased, although the average rate of refusal is about the same, i.e. 40%. One possible reason that may explain the lack of an increase in the number of patent applications being filed today is that about 70% of all patents being issued currently are filed and assigned to companies, as against 40 to 50% level prevailing in the 1930's. Patent applications are being filed more selectively on account of the growing complexity and higher quality of new inventions. Furthermore, the high standard of invention required by the Supreme Court and Federal Courts before they will sustain and enforce issued patents has caused the Patent Office to set more rigid tests for unobviousness in granting patents. It also appears that about 65% of all patents issued today represent inventions that are being commercialized (according to a recent utilization study which I have carried out for the Patent Foundation of The George Washington University). Before patent applications are actually filed, many companies place their new inventions on the market in order to determine potential markets. If the results are not favorable, patent applications are not filed. Furthermore, the cost of filing and prosecuting patent applications has risen tremendously. The cost of information retrieval has greatly increased. The existing technical literature must be considered and carefully studied in defining the novel features of new inventions as required by our patent law. Over three million U.S. patents have been issued since 1836. Complete printed copies are available to anyone at a cost of 25 cents. Any prior patent may contain anticipatory disclosures which can be cited against a pending patent application. In addition, about seven million foreign patents and an immense technical literature published in any language represent prior art that may be cited against the granting of a patent or used in invalidating an issued patent if there is anticipatory description of the same invention. In the past 25 years the cumulative search load in the U.S. Patent Office has doubled. In the chemical arts alone the literature has doubled in the last eight years. A perceptive analysis of the difficulties and uncertainties in measuring inventive activity on the basis of patent statistics is made in a paper, "Some Difficulties in Measuring Inventive Activity," by Barkev S. Sanders published in *The Rate and Direction of Inventive Activity* (1962), pages 53-90.

It is generally assumed that the issued patents which are not currently assigned to companies are owned by individual or freelance inventors. Since the patents assigned to companies have been steadily increasing from about 40 to 60% in 1935 to about 70% today, it has been inferred that the individual or independent inventor is steadily disappearing. In the past few years practically all patents in the chemical and electrical arts are assigned to companies. Over 20% of all issued patents are classified in the chemical arts and about the same percentage in the electrical arts. This leaves roughly about 50% of issued patents which are classified in the mechanical arts and it is in this area where we find most of the individual inventors working today. There is still plenty of room for creative ingenuity in the relatively simpler mechanical arts which do not require elaborate equipment or costly facilities to develop as compared with the highly complex instrumentation required to carry on research in the chemical and atomic energy fields. Hence, in these arts the inventor is usually a company employee. Furthermore, creative chemists, physicists and engineers are so eagerly sought for by industry today and are being offered such attractive research facilities and salaries that they find it expedient to accept such tempting offers, and they thus disappear as inventors working on their own.

I should like to refer also to the statistics relating to multiple inventions given in Chapter 8 of my book. According to the 1962 Fiscal Report of the Commissioner of Patents, a total of 3,265 interferences were pending in the Patent Office involving a total number of pending applications of 197,397, or 1.65%. Since at least two applications claiming the same invention are involved in each interference, at least 3% of all pending applications represent multiple inventions being made currently. Interference proceedings in the Patent Office are contests to determine the priority of a specific invention for which a patent is sought. These contests are vigorously fought at considerable cost and are decided by the Patent Office on the basis of competent, authenticated and objective evidence. It is interesting to note that scientists seek to establish priority of their discoveries by early publication and that just as in the case of inventions simultaneous discoveries are often made by independent investigators. Some interesting case histories are given by Professor K. Merton, *Priorities in Scientific Discovery,* 22 American Sociological Review December 1957, page 635.

As discussed in Chapter 7 of my book the role of chance or serendipity in invention and discovery I believe is greater than generally recognized. This subject deserves intensive study. The case histories of basic inventions and important technological breakthroughs clearly indicate that chance plays a tremendous role especially in the chemical and pharmaceutical fields. In the inventing process random or chance events may occur in the physical environment which may be observed by the aware or perceptive mind of the inventor and which may be then deliberately staged, repeated or merely re-observed and then applied for a specific useful purpose. There is no certainty in planning and predicting inventions of the type which depart radically from existing types. The so-called current planned research of industrial organizations results essentially in expected improvements and refinements of existing inventions. These are the inventions which are usually patented. They represent small but important increments to our technology. The revolutionary inventions are less foreseeable because serendipity plays a great role in their production. Some recent publications containing materials relating to the role of chance in discovery and invention are: R. Taton, *Reason and Chance in Scientific Discovery* (1957); Fernand Lot, *Les jeux du hasard et du génie* (Paris 1956); Gardner Murphy, *Human Potentialities* (1958), Chap. 7; W. B. Cannon, *The Way of an Investigator* (1945) Chap. 6; W. I. B. Beveridge, *The Art of Scientific Investigation* (1950) Chap. 3; J. S. Hadamard, *Psychology of Invention in the Mathematical Field* (1945).

During the past 25 years, few significant studies have been published relating to the work of the inventor or to the problems of developing specific inventions. To mention a few: H. Stafford Hatfield's *The Inventor and His World* (1933); C. D. Tuska, *Inventors and Inventions* (1957); Frank Cameron, *Cottrell: Samaritan* (1952); Stacy V. Jones, *You Ought to Patent That* (1962); the series of studies by Roger Burlingame deserve mention: *March of the Iron Men* (1960); *Engines of Democracy* (1940); *Machines that Built America* (1953); *Scientists Behind the Inventors* (1960); L. Sprague de Camp, *Heroic Age of American Invention* (1961); Eric Hodgins and F. A. Magoun, *Behemoth: The Story of Power* (1932); Joachim G. Leithäuser, *Inventors' Progress: The Story of Today's Revolution in Technology and of the Men Whose Originality is Transforming Our World* (1959); S. Giedion, *Mechanization Takes Command* (1948); Mitchell Wilson, *American Science and Invention: A Pictorial History* (1954); Ruth White, *Yankee from Sweden: The Dream and the Reality in the Days of John Ericsson* (1960); William Greenleaf, *Monopoly on Wheels: Henry Ford and the Selden Automobile Patent* (1961); David O. Woodbury, *Elihu Thomson: Beloved Scientist* (1960); Matthew Josephson, *Edison: A Biography* (1959); T. Coulson, *Joseph Henry: His Life and Work* (1950); E. H. Cameron, *Samuel Slater, Father of American Manufactures* (1960); Shirley Thomas, *Men of Space:*

Profiles of the Leaders of Space Research, Development and Exploration Vol. 1 (1960), Vol. 2 (1961); Robert H. Goddard, *Rocket Development: Liquid Fuel Rocket Research, 1929-1941* (1961); Edmund Fuller, *Tinkers and Genius: The Story of the Yankee Inventors* (1955); Lawrence Lessing, *Man of High Fidelity: Edwin H. Armstrong* (1956); J. J. O'Neill, *Prodigal Genius: The Life of Nikola Tesla* (1944); Orrin E. Dunlap, Jr., *Radio's 100 Men of Science* (1944); Fred C. Kelly, *The Wright Brothers* (1945); Richard W. Current, *The Typewriter and the Men Who Made It* (1954).

Several studies clearly show how the profit motive operated in specific industries to develop inventions which were patented: John L. Enos, *Petroleum Progress and Profits: A History of Process Innovation* (1962); Harold C. Passer, *The Electrical Manufacturers 1875-1900* (1953); R. Schlaifer and S. D. Heron, *The Development of Aircraft Engines and Fuels* (1950); W. Rupert Maclaurin, *Invention and Innovation in the Radio Industry* (1949); Arthur A. Bright, Jr., *The Electric-Lamp Industry: Technological Change and Economic Development from 1800 to 1947* (1949); W. Paul Strassmann, *Risk and Technological Innovation: American Manufacturing Methods during the Nineteenth Century* (1959); Virginia Huck, *Brand of the Tartan: The 3M Story* (1955); Edgar M. Queenny, *The Spirit of Enterprise* (1943); Ernest Dale, *The Great Organizers* (1960); *The Rate and Direction of Inventive Activity: Economic and Social Factors* (1962), 24 papers presented at a conference at the University of Minnesota; John B. Rae, *American Automobile Manufacturers: The First Forty Years* (1959); Richard R. Nelson, *The Economics of Invention: A Survey of the Literature* (1959); Richard G. Hubler, *Big Eight: A Biography of an Airplane* (1960). (The Douglass Company designed and built the DC-8 in six years at cost of $500 million—"the largest single venture of its kind on a single product in the world.") Tom Mahoney, *The Merchants of Life,* an account of the American pharmaceutical industry (1959).

There are few practical guides for inventors in spite of urgent need for them: Joseph C. Keeley, *Making Inventions Pay* (1950); Louis Chayka, *Inventing for Profit* (1940); Alf K. Berle and L. Sprague de Camp, *Inventions, Patents and Their Man-*

agement, (1959); *Inventors' Handbook* (1962) published by Science and Mechanics Magazine; Harry Kursh, *Inside the Patent Office* (1959); E. D. Hutchinson, *How to Think Creatively* (1949); Alex Osborn, *Applied Imagination* (1957). The last book was the basis of "brain storming" sessions which seem to be fading out. The book is useful in suggesting that a creative approach in all our activities will bring success.

In spite of the importance of technology in our lives, surprisingly little attention has been given to the history of technology. It is obvious that information relating to the growth and evolution of specific industries may shed considerable light on the environmental influences on the inventor and the complex factors which induce innovations. In 1959 the Society for the History of Technology was organized and it began publication of a very valuable quarterly journal, "Technology and Culture." This journal contains valuable original articles and excellent book reviews relating to the history of technology. In Vol. 1, pages 48-59, an article by Francis R. Allen entitled, "Technology and Social Change: Current Status and Outlook," reviews important recent books on this subject. An excellent bibliography by Thomas J. Higgins appears in Vol. 2, pages 28-32, 146-165 (1961), *A Bibliographical Bibliography of Electrical Engineers and Electrophysicists.* The study of S. C. Gilfillan, *The Sociology of Invention* (1931) is a classic. Mention must also be made of the monumental work of Charles Singer, *A History of Technology,* Vol. 1, *From Early Times to the Fall of the Ancient Empires* (1955); Vol. 2, *The Mediterranean Civilizations and the Middle Ages* (1956); Vol. 3, *From the Renaissance to the Industrial Revolution* (1957); Vol. 4, *The Industrial Revolution c. 1750 to c. 1850* (1958); and Vol. 5, *The Late Nineteenth Century c. 1850 to c. 1900* (1958). Other books deserving mention are: Fredrich Klemm, *A History of Western Technology* (1954); John W. Oliver, *History of American Technology* (1956); Robert S. Woodbury, *History of the Milling Machine* (1960); *History of the Lathe* (1961); *History of the Grinding Machine* (1959); *History of the Gear-Cutting Machine* (1958); R. J. Forbes, *Man the Maker: A History of Technology and Engineering* (1950). The U.S. National Museum has published a series of Contributions from the Museum of History and Technology starting in 1959; Heinz Gartmann, *Rings Around the World: Man's Progress from Steam Engine to Satellite* (1959).

I am confident that in the near future our current psychological research in the field of creativity will be very fruitful and will give us powerful tools that will be utilized to select creative individuals and enable us to develop a favorable environment for giving such creative individuals opportunities to use their creative abilities to their maximum capacities. The recent psychological studies relating to creativity have not yet resulted in a unified theory of creativity. Just as physicists are puzzled today by the discoveries of many so-called fundamental particles of matter, so psychologists are discovering long lists of personality factors. Professor J. P. Guilford, for example, has developed a battery of 50 different tests to test creative individuals. However, we do have fairly well generalized personality impressions of the creative person. He is a non-conformist, shows a high level of initiative and independence of thinking. He also shows curiosity, self-discipline and a drive for accomplishment. He tends to become totally involved in his work. In general, the truly creative person is not a good organization man, yet as a company employee or as a member of a large research team he is under pressure to adjust to organization life. The conventional restraints required by organization activities tend to impair his creativity because he loses more or less the freedom of action essential to creativity. He cannot always choose his own problem or satisfy his random curiosity without accounting for lost time to his superior or research director. The problem for industrial as well as private and government research management is thus to provide a creative atmosphere, taking into account the psychological factors of the inventor and at the same time not to impair the productivity of R & D personnel by requiring too rigid compliance with the work discipline imposed on non-creative employees.

It appears that in the immediate future more and more research will have to be carried out by organized research teams on account of the growing complexity of technology and the concomitant increased cost of research facilities. Effective stimulation by management of R & D personnel to create will require an appreciation of the factors involved in the creative process as well as a sympathetic understanding of the creative personality. Creativity cannot be set in motion at will or to order.

Maurice Nelles, an industrial research director, has stated:

> "The historians of the future may well select the development of deliberate creativeness as the most important development of this century. We have passed through the age of random creativeness and are entering an age of deliberate creativeness. With this technique there is almost certainty that we can fulfill our needs, desires and whims in the future. The rate at which we can develop will be increased enormously and, if the same or analogous techniques are applied to other fields, man will not only be mindful of himself, but will understand himself and his interactions with his environments. What we have today is wonderful; but what there will be tomorrow will be much better."

Professor Lynn White Jr., of the University of California, has put it more succinctly: "The analysis of the nature of creativity is one of the chief intellectual commitments of our age."

Philadelphia, Pa. JOSEPH ROSSMAN
December 1963

PREFACE

THE profound alteration in our physical environment, especially during the last hundred years, has been effected to a large extent by our inventors. It is generally acknowledged that the entire progress of the human race from primitive times to its present level has been made possible by the inventor of physical devices. As an innovator and leader, the inventor performs one of the most important functions in society, for he holds the key to further progress.

It is more than astonishing to find that practically no systematic and adequate psychological study of the inventor has been made to date, although he has been of cardinal importance to the human race. The economists, sociologists, psychologists, and anthropologists frequently refer to the inventor and they generally recognize his importance to the progress of civilization and culture. However, the mental processes of the inventor, the actual methods which he follows in making inventions, the obstacles and difficulties which he encounters, the motives which impel him to invent and many other important subjects relating to his work, have only been cursorily touched upon by the psychologists and the problem of the inventor has been dismissed with a few casual remarks and generalizations, having few facts to support them.

The object of this study is to make a pioneer contribution to the hitherto neglected subject of the psychology of the inventor. A true understanding of invention and the inventor can only come from such study. A thorough knowledge of the psychological background of the inventor will enable society to encourage invention in a truly scientific manner and make it possible to control the future progress of our civilization. It may enable us to select latent inventors and to train them, thus giving society its most powerful tool for social control.

This book has been confined principally to the inventors of physical devices who have obtained patents for their inventions. There are, of course, many inventors who make inventions which are not patentable. A study of modern industrial history, however, indicates that practically every important and significant invention falls within the field of patentable invention. The great advantage in limiting the study to patentees arises from their accessibility through the records of the Patent Office. The patentee can be readily identified with a definite invention which has received the approval of the Government. This group of inventors has also appealed personally to me on account of my official position in the United States Patent Office as Patent Examiner for the last seven years, where I have passed upon the patentability of thousands of important inventions involving commercial investments amounting to millions of dollars. My official position has also enabled me to come into intimate contact with many inventors thus giving me a good insight into their problems.

Valuable, first-hand information for this book was obtained from a group of over seven hundred inventors consisting of the most active and important inventors of this country including Dr. Elihu Thomson, Dr. Reginald Fessenden, Dr. John Hays Hammond, Jr., Dr. Miller Reese Hutchison, John F. O'Connor, Henry A. Wise Wood, Lloyd G. Copeman, Dr. I. Kitsee, Reuben B. Benjamin, Chas. C. Worthington, Frank Mossberg, Wm. F. Folmer, Harry N. Pflager, and August Sundh, who each have hundreds of patents to their credit. The conclusions derived from a study of this group of men should, therefore, be of great importance and significance as these men represent the highest class of inventors found in the industries today. The inventors displayed a very keen interest in this study and they cooperated in a most gratifying manner.

This book contains many valuable and important remarks of inventors which have never before appeared in print. A wealth of first-hand material is presented here relating to the actual methods of inventing, the mental processes of inventors, their motives and other psychological matters. This book also embodies in succinct and concise language the advice and counsel of inventors which they have acquired through many years of experience and expenditure of vast fortunes. It will warn all those who are actually inventors or would-be inventors what difficulties to avoid and how to avoid them in making inventions. A large amount of material is presented here which will be of inestimable value not only to inventors but also to engineers, mechanics, chemists, executives, and all those connected with the promotion of industrial devices.

Five hundred questionnaires were sent to the outstanding patent attorneys in the United States for further data regarding the inventor. Patent attorneys come directly in contact with numerous inventors and their observations on inventors have been found to be very useful as first-hand information.

Three hundred questionnaires were also sent to the directors of research and development departments of the largest corporations and companies in this country. The directors of these departments deal with new inventions and problems every day and they have an excellent opportunity of observing inventors at work.

It is hoped that this book will stimulate a greater interest in our inventors so that they may ultimately gain the professional recognition which has been earned but withheld too long.

I wish to acknowledge my gratitude to Dr. Knight Dunlap and Dr. John E. Bentley, of the Department of Psychology in the American University and Johns Hopkins University, for their encouragement and assistance in this work. A great deal of helpful and valuable criticism was given by Mr. Wm. I. Wyman, Principal Examiner of the United States Patent Office, who has been an official in the Patent Office for the last twenty-five years.

Mr. P. J. Federico, Patent Examiner in the United States Patent Office, also gave some useful suggestions. Finally, I wish to express my deepest thanks to my wife, who is virtually a co-author of this book. Without her encouragement, active cooperation, untiring assistance and actual personal sacrifice, this study would not have been possible.

J. R.

U. S. Patent Office
Washington, D. C.
February, 1931

PREFACE TO SECOND EDITION

The widespread interest in the subject-matter of this book as evidenced by the early exhaustion of the first edition was much greater than I had anticipated.

The entire format has been changed in the present edition. A number of corrections and additions have also been made in the text.

The deep interest of the inventors in this book has been most gratifying to me. Mr. Samuel W. Rushmore, the well-known inventor, was instrumental in disposing of many copies of the first edition.

I wish to express my appreciation to Mr. N. I. Kobin, of the W. F. Roberts Co., for his fine editorial suggestions in preparing this edition.

My thanks are also due to the critics and friends, too numerous to mention here, for their kind comments.

J. R.

U. S. Patent Office
September, 1931

CONTENTS

LIST OF TABLES

CHAPTER I

CIVILIZATION AND INVENTION

THE outstanding characteristic of our civilization is its complete dependence on invention. We are entirely surrounded by inventions and their resulting products. Our very existence, our comfort, and happiness are at the mercy of invention. Every fiber of our social system is permeated with invention. It is the keystone of our civilization and the very life-blood of its existence. Take our inventions away and we would be plunged into barbarism overnight. We would be the most helpless animal in the world. Only a handful of humanity could possibly survive such a calamity.

It is now universally acknowledged that the tremendous progress of this country, especially during the recent years, is due to invention. The recent celebration of the fiftieth anniversary of Edison's invention of the incandescent lamp, in which our whole nation participated, is characteristically indicative of our reverent attitude toward invention.

The ancients also thoroughly understood the great importance of inventions and discoveries. They honored their inventors by making them gods. The Egyptian god Osiris taught the art of farming and the use of the plough. Isis, his wife, was worshipped by multitudes in the magnificent temples of Thebes and Memphis for her discovery of wheat and barley. Prometheus, according to Greek mythology, taught the use of fire, and Daedulus the art of flying. The Bible makes a few interesting references to inventors. For instance, Tubal-cain is stated to be "an instructor of every artificer in brass and iron" in the book of Genesis. Amos tells us that David was an inventor of musical instruments. Many other examples could be given.

We cannot study the mythology of the Greeks, Romans or other groups of peoples without being impressed by the fact that many of their gods were inventors. We thus see that man realized, even in primitive times, the great importance of inventions and he expressed his respect and admiration by deifying the inventor.

Today, we occasionally honor the inventor. Yet not so many years ago he was regarded with suspicion and distrust. He was even considered by many as a danger and menace to society. Kay, the inventor of the fly-shuttle, was mobbed when he introduced his invention in Lancashire. A mob destroyed the spinning-frame invented by Hargreaves. Crampton had to hide his spinning-mule, fearing a similar fate. Jacquard barely escaped being drowned in the Rhone by angry weavers on account of his new loom. There were riots in Nottingham on account of the introduction of the stocking-loom. Fortunately, the inventor today is treated with much more consideration and respect because his economic importance is understood. It is true that some inventors have been showered with wealth, honor, and praises, but on the whole, the layman is quite oblivious of the inventor who has toiled and worked for him in the past.

How many of the 25,000,000 automobile owners today think of the countless number of inventors who worked and toiled to make the automobile possible? How many think of Charles Goodyear, the pioneer inventor, who discovered the vulcanization of rubber, thus making possible the automobile tire? How many think of his great trials, sufferings, and tribulations before he discovered how rubber could be vulcanized? How many feel grateful to him whenever they use the thousands upon thousands of articles and devices made from rubber? Very few.

The reason is obvious. We use so many inventions in our daily lives that it would be utterly impossible to give their originators even a fleeting thought. It would be taxing our minds too much.

The reason for this attitude is that inventions are part and parcel of our culture. Any contrivance that is useful to society is immediately appropriated and made part of the social culture. It becomes public property and belongs to everyone. The rapidity with which new inventions are ultimately adopted and disseminated today is remarkable and astonishing. A few years ago the automobile, the aeroplane, the telephone, the radio were unknown. Today we have millions of telephones, radios, and automobiles in use.

The human race has virtually become the inventor. The individual inventor is merely an agent who adds his feeble efforts to what has been done before. Our inventions are the result of social accretions to prior inventions. For this reason it is very often difficult, if not impossible, to say who is the inventor of any particular mechanism such as the locomotive or steamship. Countless inventors have put their energy and efforts on the locomotive or steamship, each one improving and adding new features to the mechanism which he found before him. If the machine works better, if it is more efficient and useful, it will be adopted, sooner or later. The ideal of our age is improvement and progress. It is the accepted axiom of our civilization which distinguishes it so sharply from all other civilizations that preceded ours. We believe in progress and realize it by means of inventions.

The remarkable acceleration of invention during the last hundred years is probably due to the general acceptance of the present social ideal of progress. We have become acutely aware of the fact that invention is the foundation of our culture and social progress. We see that the machine has liberated man; it has given him leisure; it has made him master over nature. We have accepted the machine as one of the essentials to our existence and have made it a permanent part of our artificial environment. Inventions have thus become our distinct cultural trait.

It is generally understood and accepted that man's rise from the plane of the animal to civilization is due entirely to his inventions, but it is remarkable that invention is still the most potent factor in the development of our present civilization. We have become so mechanized that it has been even suggested that the stage of a country's progress in civilization could be measured by the horsepower generated per each inhabitant. Inventions have caused social upheavals and changes which would have never occurred but for them. Our entire social structure has been altered indirectly during the last hundred years by our inventors and many changes are now going on so rapidly that it is difficult to even guess at their outcome.

Invention is a growth into the future which cannot be foreseen. Thousands upon thousands of inventions are made each year. The United States Patent Office is granting over 40,000 patents each year. It is difficult to forecast which one of these thousands may be of social significance. A single invention may contain in it the germ of a new development, a new industry, followed by inevitable social changes. This is clearly illustrated by the automobile, the telephone, the radio, and the movie. The diffusion of these inventions has caused changes which have altered our entire national life. They have brought with them new social problems, new situations which require solution. New inventions are social ferments bringing about new changes in the existing social structure. These changes begin in an incomprehensible and almost unnoticeable manner. The new invention is accepted only by a few individuals at first and is gradually adopted by all. This process is easily demonstrated by the spread of the automobile which was at first just a curiosity.

Only a few generations ago the so-called "horseless carriage" was very much ridiculed. The interchange of goods and commodities was slow and difficult. There were no good roads, no ways to travel safely and swiftly, but as the automobile became more developed and perfected by our inventors and its great utility was demonstrated, it began to be taken seriously. More and more people began to utilize it, as it had many obvious advantages over the horse-drawn vehicles. In a few years we find over 25,000,000 automobiles on our roads and streets. The hills were leveled, the horizons extended and new opportunities created. Our country became united as it never was before. The city streets have become congested and serious problems have arisen. Traffic laws had to be enacted. Thousands upon thousands of garages and gas stations appeared everywhere. Our magazines are filled with automobile advertisements. The States have been linked by thousands upon thousands of miles of new roads. Rural and city life has been changed. Intercourse has increased by leaps and bounds. Transactions are made swiftly. The obstacles of distance have been minimized. The city has been brought to the farmer. The esthetic taste of the people has been enormously educated by the products of the rival concerns who are doing all they can to appeal to the eye of the public. The industries, too, have been profoundly altered. The vast number of new materials manufactured for the automobile is amazing. New steel alloys, paints and lacquers, glass and fabrics, have been created for it. The automobile has become a synthesis of thousands of inventions integrated into an organic unit. New factories have arisen to supply these materials and inventions. New machines had to be designed to produce these demands. Powerful corporations have arisen which exert an enormous influence on the economic life of the entire Nation.

A new invention, such as the automobile, can thus become a great social disturber and stimulator. Its effects are profound and cumulative. The effects of a new invention react not only on itself but also on all other inventions. It is merely one of the many forces liberated by countless inventions reacting together in a complex manner in the life of our society.

The changes thus made by inventors are entirely unintended and unforeseen. Inventors are unconscious social changers. Their origin is uncontrollable. No one can stop them. They seem to have a peculiar law of their own. Each new invention may become the focus of a new social pulsation which may shake the very foundations of society.

Our civilization is a synthesis of inventions and it is therefore highly necessary for us to understand the nature of invention and the psychology of the inventor. If we hope to exert a scientific control of our progress and development we must do so by means of inventions. In order to grow and develop we must have more inventions. To have the necessary inventions at our command, we must have the inventors and give them the proper conditions in which to invent. At present we know practically nothing of the psychological process involved in inventing, the conditions favorable to invention, the peculiarities and characteristics of the inventor, his methods of inventing, his education or training.

Is the inventor different from other people? Has he the so-called "inventive faculty" which causes him to invent? Or is it a normal human activity? We do not know the first thing about the art of invention. It has been so far an entirely empirical and haphazard art. Although inventors have given us everything we have today in the form of material and spiritual culture, yet we have taken very little trouble to study or understand them. We have overlooked the most vital and important factor in the development of our civilization. The inventor is the true benefactor of man and the builder of civilization. Every invention he makes is another gift to his generation as well as to posterity. The inventor has lifted man from a filthy precarious animal existence to the possibility of living as a rational human being. For these reasons we propose to study the psychology of the inventor in the following pages. But before we do so, it will be necessary for us to clearly understand what is meant by invention. This will be discussed in the next chapter.

CHAPTER II

What Is Invention?

THE term *invention* is one of the most elusive words in the English language. It is as difficult to define as the word life. We all know what life is, but how many can define it? In the same way, nearly everyone has some idea of the meaning of invention, but the average person would find great difficulty in defining it.

The fundamental concept underlying invention is that it is something new or novel. In this sense invention embraces nearly all of human activity. It is not necessarily limited to developments in the physical sciences or in the industries, as it is ordinarily assumed. The term invention embraces all new developments in the social, administrative, business, the technical, scientific, and esthetic fields. It is applicable to all constructive intellectual work such as a new picture, statue, novel, poem, or song, and a new scientific method or theory, a law which will result in a useful economic or social effect, a legal system or government, a scheme of advertising or doing business, a new system of banking or finance, a method of teaching children, a new machine, a new chemical process, a system of philosophy. We do not ordinarily designate new developments in the social, esthetic, administrative, and business fields as inventions. This term is usually confined by most people to the technical field such as a new machine or process and it is very often identified with patented inventions, but as it has been just pointed out, the word has a much broader scope in its meaning.

Inventions may be divided into the physical, the social, and the mental. Each one of these groups deals with different fields of human activity. The physical inventions include all new devices or methods depending on the physical materials or forces found in nature such as machinery, chemical or electrical processes. This group includes all inventions falling in the field of patents and also many others which are not patentable.

The social inventions have to do with human relations such as marriage, law, government, business, and finance. A new tariff law which would please every one in this country and every one in foreign countries would, for example, be a great social invention.

Mental inventions deal with ideas such as scientific theories, systems of philosophy, esthetic productions in art and literature.[1]

The outstanding feature of all inventions is that they give something which has not existed before. Things or ideas are fitted together, interwoven and combined to produce results which are more than the details from which they are formed. Old and well-known elements are combined into new combinations or patterns giving a new result or synthesis. The elements used to make the new combinations may be taken from the field of any human activity. Let us take, for instance, language or music. Although there are only twenty-six letters in our alphabet, hundreds of thousands of words have been made by the permutation and combination of these letters. The words found in the dictionary are further combined to make sentences, paragraphs, and books to serve all possible human needs. Similarly, in music we have the scale which consists of a number of elementary and well-defined notes. The same notes are found in every musical composition, no matter how old or new it may be. The simple folk-songs and the most complicated modern symphony are built from the same notes. The only thing that is new in each is the new combination of notes, the new patterns. The composer creates his new compositions by merely giving us new arrangements of

---

[1] L. L. Bernard, An introduction to social psychology, New York, Holt, 1926, 165.

old notes. Any other invention, no matter in what field it is found, can be reduced similarly to elementary and old units or elements. A complicated textile machine or locomotive can be taken apart until it will be nothing more than a heap of well-known machine-elements such as gears, cams, pulleys, rods, links, shafts, etc. The machine-elements were well known before these machines were invented and the invention, therefore, consists in the way these elements were combined and arranged to produce a new result.

In the same way, a new scientific theory is an invention built from known facts of human knowledge. The periodic table of chemical elements made by Mendeléeff is built up from known chemical symbols. The chemical elements were classified and arranged in many ways before Mendeléeff, but he made a new arrangement of the elements which was very useful to chemists. It caused them to look at the chemical elements in a new way. New relationships were seen, new possibilities arose which were not evident before. Thus it is possible to produce new knowledge by a combination of known facts. This is as much invention as it is to produce a new machine from gears, belts, pulleys, nuts, etc. Inventions, therefore, may be made by combining any known ideas or elements into a new system or pattern. An invention gives us new relations of old elements, new ways of using known things for our greater advantage and benefit.

The concept underlying invention can be very well brought out by observing what happens in the making of a new chemical compound made from two known elements. Water, for instance, can be made by mixing hydrogen and oxygen gases in a container and exploding the mixture by means of an electric spark. The gases disappear and water exists in their place. Before the explosion we had two different gases, each having its characteristic and peculiar qualities. Now, after the explosion, we have them combined in a new way, producing something entirely different from what existed before. The water has properties different from both the hydrogen and oxygen. It has an individuality of its own, although both hydrogen and oxygen still exist in its component molecules as such. This is exactly what we have in an invention. We take old elements, ideas, things or whatever you please and combine them into new forms, combinations or patterns having a distinct individuality, new qualities, new properties which the separate components do not have.

Thus far, we have been regarding invention from the detached objective viewpoint. We have been looking at the mere results of invention without noting any other possible aspects. The term *invention* has several distinct meanings. It is for this reason that so much confusion arises when a definition of invention is attempted. It may refer to:

1. the thing invented,
2. the quality or property of the invention,
3. the mental processes,
4. the ability to invent,
5. the historical fact that an invention has been made.

The use of the word invention to designate that which has been invented is one of its common and obvious uses. In this sense when we refer to the invention of the linotype machine we mean the machine itself, as it stands before us, as an assembly of many machine elements and mechanisms. It is the final product of the inventive process and is complete in itself. It is in this sense that we have thus far been discussing the meaning of invention.

The mental or psychological aspect of invention is the most important and fundamental one for us to regard in this study. We are not so much interested in the inventions themselves as we are in the mental processes which evolved them. The psychological definition of invention will not be discussed here but it will be given in Chapter

VI where the psychological factors of invention will be studied. It is important for the present, however, to keep this meaning of the word invention in mind.

We may speak, for instance, of the invention of the linotype machine by Mergenthaler to indicate all the mental as well as actual steps he took in perfecting his device. We also speak of the invention of the steam-engine or the automobile. Here no single individual can be said to be the inventor. The steam-engine and automobile are the results of the inventive efforts of many men; each one adding something to what was done before him, but no one man can be credited for the complete invention. The invention of the steam-engine thus refers to the entire evolution of the steam-engine from its crude beginnings to its perfected form today, which actually consists of an assemblage of many inventions. It includes the inventive efforts of Papin, Newcomen, Watt, Corliss and scores of other men extending over a long period of time. The term invention thus has a very flexible meaning. It may embrace the successive efforts expended by many men on the same problem during many generations, or it may refer to the inventive act of a man exerted for five minutes or for many years.

The third meaning of the word invention refers to the quality or the property of the invention. Thus we may say that the telegraph shows invention over all prior devices. By this we mean that the telegraph is the final product or embodiment of all the psychological processes of the inventor as well as of the previously known physical elements in its structure of which it is actually made.

Invention may also be used to signify the ability to invent. The so-called "faculty of invention" means that a person has the ability to produce inventions. This meaning is so closely tied up with the psychological aspect of invention that the two can be regarded as the same thing for all practical purposes.

The various meanings of the word invention can be best illustrated by a simple example as follows: The statement that "the linotype machine is the invention of Mergenthaler," refers to the mental process which produced it. When we say "It was a useful invention," we refer to the machine itself, and when we say "The invention of the linotype machine revolutionized printing methods" we refer to the historical fact that it was made. If we say that the "particular form of the machine before us presents no invention over a previous one," we refer to the quality of invention as distinguished from the mental act, the thing itself, and the historical fact.

It is important to note the relative meaning of invention from the individual and the social or cultural viewpoint. When we define invention as something new, what do we mean by new? A man, for example, may construct a pump which to his knowledge is absolutely new. He has never read about such a pump and he has never seen one in use. This man has actually created this machine by his own mental processes without receiving direct suggestions from any source whatsoever. Let us assume that he has spent years of his time and thousands of dollars to build and perfect his pump. But if we should search the Patent Office records we would find an exact description of the same pump made a hundred years before. Our inventor has in this case re-invented the machine, and, as far as he is concerned and from the psychological viewpoint, he is a true inventor. But, what has he added to our fund of knowledge and to our cultural achievement? Nothing. From the cultural viewpoint, therefore, this man has made no invention. This relative meaning of invention is often overlooked. Invention must pass the cultural test of novelty in order to be recognized as a new invention. Our standard of novelty is continually changing as each new invention is made public and becomes added to the common stock of knowledge. When inventions are patented or adopted by society they become part of our culture and general fund of knowledge. We even fail to look at them as inventions as time goes on. How many people regard clothes, drinking vessels, bottles, knives, forks, or hammers as inventions? They are taken for granted as well-known and useful objects which are found everywhere. Yet at one time they did not exist. They had to be invented and adopted. Their utility had to be learned by the mass of the people until they became part of our culture which is passed on from generation to generation. We still look on the telephone and the telegraph as inventions but undoubtedly as they will be continued to be used for several more generations they will hardly be regarded as such in the future as they are today.

Inventions can also be divided into two broad groups—pioneer or basic inventions and improvement or intensive inventions. The first class of inventions are the revolutionary inventions which are distinct and epoch-making landmarks in human progress. The invention of written language was a basic invention. It made civilization possible. The telephone, the phonograph, and the movie are good examples of basic physical inventions. Before these inventions were made there was absolutely nothing hinting or suggesting them. No one could have predicted or foreseen their creation. No actual demand existed before they were made except, of course, the fundamental human wants. Basic inventions usually employ new principles or they employ old principles in new and useful applications. The application of the electromagnet for transmitting signals in the telegraph, for example, was a basic invention because electromagnets were never used for this purpose before, although electromagnets themselves were known. Basic inventions often have an accidental origin because they are based on the accidental discovery of new principles or forces. The function of the inventor in this case is to appreciate the significance of the discovery which he has observed and to visualize the specific application of his discovery to practical purposes. Basic inventions, therefore, are really in the nature of discoveries. The inventor may not only discover the new principle, but he also discovers its mode of application for practical purposes and where the application of the discovery is obvious, he appreciates its practical possibilities at once.

Most inventions today are the improvement or intensive inventions which add to or improve the existing inventions. They may be made by systematic research and investigation. The numerous improvements made in the industries, such as labor-saving machinery or machines to increase the output of goods, usually fall in this class. They merely improve and intensify the results begun by the basic invention. Improvement inventions are chiefly due to competition in industry. The desire to produce better and more efficient devices brings about many refinements, additions or eliminations of the basic invention which is usually very crude when first invented. Improvement inventions are thus transformations or natural evolutions of the basic inventions.

Basic inventions in industry, on the other hand, do not result from competition. They begin new industries and create new demands. This is well illustrated by the automobile, the telephone, and the radio.

Inventions can also be classified as empirical and systematic. Many basic inventions especially in primitive times were empirical in nature. This was necessarily due to their dependence on accidental discoveries and lack of scientific knowledge. Even today we have empirical inventions made by cut and try methods, which is a process of approximation and elimination. These inventions are crude at first and are perfected as they are being used.

Systematic or projected inventions are the outstanding feature of our age. This is particularly true of our physical inventions. These inventions are made by professional inventors who are well versed in all details of their problems. The commercial corporations are employing thousands of men whose job it is to invent. Almost unlimited facilities and means are placed at their disposal. These men not only improve existing inventions but they often produce new applications in the industries. They have made new alloys and compounds. They produce automatic machinery such as automatic screw-cutting machines, high-production tire making machines, and so forth. Very often a great deal of research is made in the pure sciences merely for the purpose of possibly applying the discoveries to practical and commercial uses. This is particularly true in the chemical industries which employ thousands of chemists searching for new materials or products. The extraordinary use of the new lacquers used on automobiles, the marvelous production of artificial silks, the manufacture of Bakelite and other synthetic resins, the electroplating with chromium and cadmium have all been made possible during the last few years by patient and systematic research. They are typical projected inventions.

This brings us to a consideration of discovery and research. Although these are distinct from invention proper, they are important factors essential to invention.

Research is a systematic investigation for the purpose of discovery, and discovery is the finding of new facts. Discoveries may obviously also be accidental findings of new facts. We find by research or discovery what has existed before and what is inherent in the nature of things but has been unknown. Discoveries thus increase our fund of knowledge. They may not necessarily have a practical utility in themselves. Thus many of the achievements in pure science are discoveries. The objects of research and invention are quite different. Research is seeking new knowledge, while invention is the application of existing knowledge to practical ends. When important new knowledge is discovered through research, invention may very often follow. This distinction between research and invention is generally recognized by all the research departments of the large corporations, which have realized that research has become an important factor in modern business.

The industrial organizations of our country employ altogether about thirty thousand research workers and spend huge sums each year on pure research. This sum has been estimated to be nearly $200,000,000 a year. The American Telephone and Telegraph Co. alone spends nearly $13,000,000 a year for research.[2] Much of the knowledge so obtained is never applied for practical purposes but what is used for commercial applications more than pays for the entire expenses of the total research. The type of research engaged in by the commercial organizations is not of the academic kind for the sake of pure science. It may be termed technical or industrial research which has been conducted during the last fifty years by the industrial organizations. It is not the research of a single man but the cooperative research of thousands of men engaged in making discoveries in all the industrial fields for their practical application. Although this kind of research is not conducted with the unselfish and disinterested motives of the pure scientist but rather for greater profits in dollars and cents yet the public is eventually benefited thereby.

In most historical cases, discoveries and their consequential inventions have been made by different individuals. Faraday discovered electromagnetic induction in 1831 but almost thirty-nine years elapsed before a successful dynamo was invented utilizing this discovery. However, the discovery and invention may be made by the same man. Thus, Edison not only discovered that carbon in thread form could be used as an electric filament but he also made a practical application of this discovery in making his incandescent lamp. In this case Edison deliberately set out to investigate all possible materials for use as a filament. He could not make his electric lamp until he found the proper material and he was, therefore, forced to become an investigator in order to solve his problem. Thus an inventor may be an in-

[2] F. W. Wile, A century of industrial progress, New York, Doubleday, 1928, 314.

vestigator, but only for practical purposes. This is exactly what industrial research means. The scientist or abstract investigator seeks knowledge with no other objective in mind. The inventor and the commercial research worker seek knowledge for utilizing it only for practical purposes. The inventor's objective is to produce, the scientist's objective is to explain and understand facts. That is why the scientist is seldom an inventor of commercial devices, because he is more interested in causes and effects than in their practical applications. The inventor, on the other hand, turns knowledge to useful purposes. He is seldom interested in the underlying theory and explanation of his invention except in so far as it has any direct bearing on the practical utility of the invention.

We must, however, not forget that although scientists do not usually make practical or commercial inventions yet the scientific instruments and apparatus devised by them in their work show the highest degree of invention. We have only to mention the galvanometer, the Leyden jar, the spectroscope, the air pump, etc.

There is no exact order for the appearance of discovery and invention. They may be made simultaneously or they may precede or follow each other in any order. Goodyear, for example, discovered accidentally that sulfur will vulcanize rubber when they are heated together and he at once applied this discovery for practical purposes. In this case once the discovery was made, the invention became immediately apparent. This discovery was actually made by Goodyear during his indefatigable attempts to vulcanize rubber. The exact theory or explanation of the vulcanization of rubber has not as yet been discovered. The vulcanization of rubber was thus a purely empirical invention.

The invention of the Voltaic pile, the discovery of aniline dye by Perkin, the production of aluminum were empirical inventions. The scientific explanations for these inventions were made quite some time later. It has already been pointed out that discoveries may often precede inventions as shown by the radio or the dynamo.

Hitherto, it has been frequently repeated that science is solely responsible for the technical advances in our industries. This statement has been made so often that most people accept it as axiomatic. Actual facts, however, do not warrant this assumption. First of all, science is merely organized knowledge; it merely describes or explains; it answers the question why things happen but it seldom tells us how to do things. It is the function of the inventor to teach us how to apply for practical purposes the knowledge which science gives us. Very few basic inventions can be attributed to pure science. Nearly all our fundamental inventions were made before there was any semblance of science. Science is still attempting to explain many inventions which have been made empirically.

Scientists have unquestionably performed miracles, and they have extended our knowledge into unknown realms. However, knowledge alone, no matter how penetrating and astounding it may be, never gives rise to new inventions or industries. It is usually left to the inventor to utilize the facts and principles of science, and to apply them for practical purposes.

Solid carbon dioxide was known to chemists for many years, but it took the perspicacity and vision of an inventor to understand the significance of its properties and its commercial possibilities in the form of "dry ice." The papers in the Patent Office give mute testimony to this.

Scientists knew for a long time that when gases expand they absorb heat, and thus cool whatever they contact, but it took an inventor to apply this knowledge in devising a commercial refrigeration system. Carbon was known to be a poor conductor of electricity, but it took an Edison to make the electric lamp, using a carbon filament. The explosive force of certain gases was known for hundreds of years, but we had to wait for an inventor to show us how this force could be harnessed in a gas engine or in an automobile. The force of steam was known by the ancients, but it was never utilized for lifting the burden from man's back until a brilliant Englishman invented the steam-engine. Man has seen birds fly for thousands of years, but we waited for the Wright brothers to show us how to do it. Electro-magnets and diaphragms were known to all physicists and electrical engineers, but they did not make a telephone until Bell showed them how. Chemists experimented with all sorts of resinous substances made artificially, but Leo Baekeland taught them how to make a new product from phenol, known all over the world as Bakelite. The alchemists several hundred years ago were familiar with phosphorus, but it never occurred to them to make matches. We had to wait for an inventor to do that. Primitive man saw logs floating day after day, but it took an unknown inventor to see in this the possibility of making a boat.

We might continue indefinitely with examples, but it is important to note that all our industries are merely developments initiated by inventors.

We have already seen that there are many different fields of invention. An important class of inventions on account of its industrial and economic significance is the field of patentable inventions. Nearly all our physical and technical inventions fall in this field. Physical inventions were the earliest inventions made by man in his struggle for existence. When primitive man seized a fallen limb of a tree to ward off a beast of prey he made a physical invention. Dead limbs were lying about for thousands of years but they were never applied to a useful purpose until our primitive inventor saw their utility and made actual use of them. Now suppose that this inventor found a certain stone with which he could sharpen the end of his tree limb. He now had a very effective tool which could easily penetrate the bodies of wild beasts and kill them. We can imagine that the fellow friends of our primitive inventor immediately saw the great advantage of the new spear. They would naturally desire to possess sharp-pointed spears but unfortunately they did not know how to make them. We can readily see how popular our primitive inventor would become with all his fellow friends flocking to him in order to be shown how to make the new spear. In a short time he would be held in great esteem and honor. He would probably be relieved of the every-day and ordinary obligations and duties of his fellow men for the rest of his life and perhaps receive other rewards such as a few more wives.

We see in this hypothetical story the beginning of the modern patent system which has the dual purpose of rewarding the inventor as well as instructing and benefiting the public. If an inventor makes a patentable invention today he can obtain a legal document called letters patent. A patent in this country is a contract between the Government and the inventor, whereby the inventor agrees to disclose his invention to the public so that the public may learn how to use the new invention and the Government agrees to give the inventor in return a monopoly for seventeen years during which time he has a right to prevent anyone else from making, using or selling his invention unless he gives him permission to do so.

Since we are making a study of the inventor who has received a patent from our Government, and who is therefore called the patentee, as he is designated in legal nomenclature, it is important for us to understand just what is meant by patentable inventions and what kind of inventions are included in this field.

The definition of patentable inventions will be found by studying our patent laws and decisions of the courts. Our patent laws are based on the provision in our Federal Constitution stating that "Congress shall have power to promote the progress of science and useful arts, by securing for limited times to authors and inventors the exclusive right to their respective writings and discoveries." The modern patent system is an ingenious legal invention itself and like most inventions it has had a long history. The American patent system is largely based on the English system which originated from the grant of monopolies by the King of England as he saw fit. This power was greatly misused by the King for personal gain. This abuse was ended by the enactment of the Statute of Monopolies by Parliament in 1624 which repealed all existing monopolies and permitted monopolies only to the inventors of new manufactures or articles not known or used before. This was the basis of the English patent system and as we have seen from the provision in the American Constitution it is also the basis of our patent system.

According to the law today a patent may be obtained by any person, irrespective of age, sex or race, who has invented any new and useful method or process, machine, manufactured article, or composition of matter, or any new and useful improvements of these. Ornamental designs for manufactured articles, and, according to a recent law, certain kinds of living plants can also be patented.

The field of patentable inventions is definitely restricted by our patent laws to these limited classes of invention. There are many inventions which cannot be patented under the present laws. Some of the most brilliant discoveries of scientists are not patentable because they do not contain certain subject-matter defined by our patent laws.

If a new and revolutionary law of nature were discovered today it could not be patented. A patent can not be granted for the law utilized, but only for the method or apparatus for utilizing the law to give a new and useful result. The Government says, in effect, to the inventor: "Tell the public how to carry out your process or how to construct your machine and you will get your patent. If you have discovered a new principle or a new process devise some means to utilize it and to carry it out for a useful purpose. The world has plenty of ideas and suggestions but what we want is their actual application in physical and useful form." The patent law thus requires the inventor to inform and teach the public how to carry out his new ideas. It does not ask him why he takes certain steps or what his theory may be. The object of the patent laws is fundamentally to instruct the public. The Government, as has already been stated, in granting an inventor a patent really enters into a contract with him whereby the inventor agrees to disclose fully his invention to the public in return for which the Government gives him a monopoly for seventeen years. At the end of this period his invention becomes public property and can be used by anyone.

An analysis of our patent laws shows that patents can be granted only for the following classes of invention:

1. Art (i. e. method or process)
2. Machine
3. Manufacture
4. Composition of matter
5. Ornamental designs
6. Certain types of living plants.

It will be seen at once that there are many inventions which are not patentable, especially those found in the social, business, intellectual, esthetic and scientific fields. Anything purely mental is not patentable. The mere discovery of a new principle, no matter how revolutionary it may be, if not connected with mechanism in order to apply it for practical purposes is not patentable.

It is very important, therefore, to understand the nature of inventions, which are included in the statutory classes of inventions just listed, for they are the only types of invention which can be patented. Mere ideas, mental concepts, systems of doing business, principles of nature, are not patentable. Each class of invention will now be discussed in order to clarify what it includes.

One of the definitions given by Webster of the word *art* is as follows: "The employment of means to accomplish some desired end, the adaptation of things in the natural world—to the uses of life, the application of knowledge or power to practical purposes." The word *art*, however, has a narrower meaning in the patent laws, and it is limited to a process or method of treatment of material things to produce definite, tangible results. The process may be a single act or a series of acts to produce a definite result. Thus we can have a process for making artificial silk, plating silver, and vulcanizing rubber.

It is almost unnecessary today to define a *machine*. We are constantly using machines in our daily lives. The term *machine* in patent law includes all mechanical powers and devices to perform some function or to produce a certain effect or result. A sewing-machine, for example, is made up of many rods, levers, cams and wheels all cooperating and co-acting so as to make the needle stitch with the thread. Every time the treadle of the sewing-machine is actuated the mechanical elements in the machine move in a pre-determined and designed manner. In other words the invention in a machine resides in so associating the elements that they will have an inherent law of operation. The sewing-machine cannot saw wood or print books because it has been designed by the inventor to do only one thing. He has so arranged and associated the different parts of the machine that when set in motion it will produce by its own operation certain pre-determined results. A machine is a sort of an artificial organism having its own laws of existence.

The term *manufactures* in patent law comprises articles or implements made by a human agency from raw or prepared materials. It embraces whatever is made by the art or industry of man, except a machine or a composition of matter. It differs from a machine in not having an inherent law of motion. For example, a table, a picture-frame, a screw-driver are articles of manufacture.

The term *composition of matter* embraces all compositions or intermixtures of two or more substances or ingredients. The properties of the resultant composition usually differ from that of each of its individual ingredients. A new cement or paint, for instance, is a composition of matter. A new chemical compound, such as a dyestuff, is also included in this class.

The foregoing classes of invention discussed embrace practically all the patents granted today and they are, therefore, the most important for our present purposes, because they contain all physical inventions. A small number of patents are granted each year for ornamental designs used in connection with articles of commerce. These patents are usually designated as "design patents" in order to distinguish them from the usual patents. Very recently an amendment to our patent laws has also given the Patent Office authority to grant patents for living plants which are asexually reproduced, other than tuber-propagated. This includes new varieties of fruits and flowers which are produced by hybridizing known plants. At the time of this writing only one "plant patent" has been granted, but no doubt many more will be granted in the near future.

The courts have had great difficulty in many cases in which patents were involved to decide whether or not they involved invention. As one judge has said: "It is very difficult to define what invention is. It certainly is not reasoning. It does not arise from any logical deduction. A necessary conclusion from certain admitted premises will not support it. Inferences such as man of ordinary intellect would naturally draw when he is possessed of the ordinary skill and knowledge of the art in respect to which the inference may be drawn, fall very short of being invention. But if we create not only by the operation of mind, but as well actually, physically, new means by which is necessarily obtained a certain specific end, means which are novel to the creator as well as to the world, which had never existed before, at least in the combination or in conjunction in which the creator causes them to exist for the first time, he who does this must, I think, be regarded as an inventor." [3]

Finding it impossible to define *invention* the courts have resorted to the opposite method by defining what is not invention. In this way a number of well-defined and clear rules or tests have been formulated. The basic rule in patent law is that the exercise of ordinary mechanical skill is not invention. Thus a machine which could be made by any mechanic when faced with a certain need would not be patentable because it merely involved ordinary mechanical skill. Making parts stronger or lighter, duplicating parts, changing the size or degree of known devices, omitting parts, changing their location, making them integral or adjustable or substituting them by a known equivalent is not considered to involve any invention because these changes are specific cases of mechanical skill. Replacing one material by another or giving it a better finish would be obvious to anyone and, therefore, not patentable. However, if the results produced by these changes are new and unexpected they will usually be regarded as patentable because in such cases they involve more than the ordinary mechanical skill of the workers in their respective fields. These rules are at best rough and ready objective tests to determine whether invention is present in any given case and in the final analysis the courts actually look to the mental process of the inventor to determine whether he used his "inventive faculty." Since we are interested in the psychological aspect of invention it will be useless to discuss these negative rules in detail here and we shall begin with the inventor himself.

[3] Dick vs. Fuerth, 57 Fed. Rep. 834.

CHAPTER III

Classes of Inventors

VERY shortly after this study was begun it became apparent that there were several distinct classes of patentees or inventors who produce patentable inventions. It will, therefore, be necessary to differentiate these groups before we proceed further.

Inventors [1] can be divided into two main classes: 1, the individual inventor; and 2, the group inventor. The individual inventor works alone relying on his own means and resources. The group inventor is the hired inventor working in cooperation with other men in a large industrial organization. The class of individual inventors includes several distinct types, such as, the old fashioned "Yankee inventor," who worked in a cut and try manner relying on his native ingenuity; the "free-lance inventor," who is the present-day representative of the "Yankee inventor"; the "casual inventor," who invents either by chance or when some unusual circumstances arise and who would otherwise never think of inventing anything; the "professional inventor," who makes inventing his sole business; and the "industrial inventor," who is a manufacturer or a worker in the industry. The industrial inventor may originally come from any of the other classes of individual inventors. As a manufacturer he invents either to improve his products or his machinery to fight competition. The worker in the factory whether he is employed as a foreman, manager, machinist, chemist, or engineer is also an industrial inventor. They invent as a matter of routine as problems arise in

[1] This term will, hereafter, be used to designate patentees, unless otherwise specified. This use of the word corresponds very closely with the popular use of the word.

their work and not because they were hired to invent. A brief description of the different classes will now be given.

The so-called "Yankee inventor" is a well-known and famous type of inventor who has been responsible for the early industrial progress of our country. We have only to mention Howe, who invented the sewing-machine, Whitney and his cotton-gin, Goodyear, the inventor of the vulcanization of rubber, Morse and his telegraph, Westinghouse and his airbrake. These men exemplify the typical Yankee inventor, working alone in unknown fields by a cut and try manner in a very empirical fashion. They were pioneers; they had to rely on their own resources and ability. They founded most of our important industries. Their means and knowledge were limited, and difficulties and troubles beset them at every step. The "Yankee inventor" was the only type of inventor known until within fifty years ago, when he gradually began to diminish in number as well as in importance. In the days of the Yankee inventor there were no great engineering schools where he could learn the fundamentals of engineering and science. Technical knowledge was very meager and limited. The inventor was, therefore, forced to employ empirical methods. He made many guesses, many attempts, and, naturally, many failures. No wonder that only so few achieved success and so many got into bad repute. We must, however, not forget our debt to the clever "Yankee inventor" who, in spite of all difficulties, gave us most of our basic inventions.

The achievements of the successful "Yankee inventor" have made such a deep impression on our industrial history that he is regarded as the ideal inventor by thousands of would-be free-lance inventors today, who cling to his old-fashioned methods. They imagine that it is not necessary to know the fundamentals of physics, chemistry, and engineering to invent. They actually believe it would be a hindrance. Year after year these free-lance inventors come from farms, factories and shops expecting to revolutionize the world by their impractical inventions and relying on the innate ingenuity which they believe they possess. Many of these men persist for years in working on their supposed inventions in vain, constituting our typical chronic and "crank inventors" who appeal so much to the public imagination.

We must remember, however, that the old-time successful "Yankee inventors" were practical men. They were attempting to solve needs that actually existed and problems that were waiting to be solved. A large majority of the unsuccessful free-lance inventors today, however, instead of seeking to meet a real need that exists, lie awake nights trying to find something to invent in order to become rich overnight. Instead of inventing something which is really needed they merely invent new needs and then proceed to meet these needs by some outlandish contrivance.

The casual inventor may come from all walks of life. He invents because he is faced with an actual need or problem which requires a solution. The lawyer, the clerk, the storekeeper, the business man, the salesman, the professor would never think of making an invention but for the problem which arises. Spurred on by such a situation he may make an invention based on a discovery made by him purely by chance or accident.

The professional inventor is a very recent development in industry. He is usually a technically trained man such as an engineer or chemist; at least, he is well informed technically. He may work systematically as an individual for himself or in cooperation with other men in a research organization, in which case he becomes a unit in a group of men who are developing new inventions, and he may, therefore, in the latter case be termed a "group inventor." The professional inventor regards inventing as a serious business. Thomas A. Edison is probably the inventor of the business of inventing. He has made inventing a profession in itself. The first $40,000 which he made from his stock-ticker was spent in equipping his laboratory with all necessary chemicals and devices for experimental work, without regard to any specific industrial purpose. His work was merely to invent for practical purposes. "If it can be done, is it worth doing?" is the first question he asks when faced with a new problem. If it was, all his energy and ability were thrown into an extended systematic search for the solution of the problem. In developing his incandescent electric lamp between three thousand and four thousand samples of suitable materials from all parts of the world were tried out. When he searched for the best material for his phonograph records he sent men to India, China, Africa and other parts of the world to find suitable vegetable wax bases.

Edison's attitude toward inventing is well illustrated by the following statement attributed to him: "Invention is the hardest kind of work and requires intense application of every faculty. There is no guesswork about it. There is no unfailing principle of luck in it. The goal must be reached by a process of elimination. Every factor must be studied, examined, and then eliminated if it is not what you want, until you have narrowed the entire problem down to two or three points. Then it is possible that luck or accident may play a minor part, and some day the whole thing will dawn upon your mind and you see the goal you have been working for." [2]

The chief difference between the individual professional inventor and the group inventor is that the former is not in the employ of a commercial organization. His field is, therefore, not limited or confined in any way. He will tackle everything and anything he sees fit. The group inventor, however, is employed to invent in certain specific lines in which his company is engaged. His field of activity is, therefore, restricted and it is probably for this reason that the large research organizations have

[2] C. O. Tessier, The patent business, New York, Printing Dept., Salvation Army, 1921, 24.

failed to produce many basic inventions. The group inventor becomes so well informed in his special field that he becomes conservative and tends to follow the beaten path ceasing to have an original and fresh outlook on his problems.

The organized and systematic research of the large industrial organizations has not yet given us many epoch-making or basic inventions. The telegraph companies did not invent the cable or the telephone. In fact, the telephone was rejected by the telegraph and cable companies when it was offered to them for $300,000. The gas companies did not invent the electric light. The steam turbine was not invented by the steam-engine manufacturers. The horse-car railways did not invent the electric railway. The silk manufacturers did not invent artificial silk. Many other instances can be given showing that the large research organizations did not produce very many of our basic inventions. This may seem to be very surprising at first. It apparently tends to show that large research organizations possess little inventive ability and will not produce many revolutionary inventions. We must, however, remember that the research organizations of the large corporations are chiefly concerned with developing and improving the inventions on which they are founded and that they do not attempt or aim to produce epoch-making new inventions because such inventions if made would not be in their line of business. Recently, however, many large corporations have entered into several unrelated fields of activity. The General Motors Corporation, for instance, besides manufacturing automobiles, is also engaged in the electric refrigerating business and recently it has entered the radio field. This tendency to spread into different unrelated fields will tend to remove many of the conservative policies of the large corporations, especially in regard to new inventions, and it may lead to the development of basic inventions.

The development of our gigantic telephone system by the research activity of the American Telegraph and Telephone Company from the invention of Bell is a good example of the achievement of group invention. As more and more telephones began to be used, innumerable problems arose. The transmitter was perfected. Complicated switch-boards had to be developed. We are now witnessing the installation of the automatic telephone for eliminating the telephone operator entirely. We can telephone to London, Paris, and Berlin today because of the invention of the thermionic telephone repeater made since Bell invented the telephone. New cables have been designed and multiplex circuit apparatus developed. Important alloys, such as permalloy, have been invented. Television and radio telephoning are now being investigated and developed for commercial purposes.

According to Dr. Grosvenor [3] a tabulation of the revolutionary inventions made since 1889, when large corporate investigation may be said to have started, shows that 12 out of the 72 outstanding inventions have been produced by corporation research. During the same period, independent inventors working "on their own," contributed such inventions as: monotype, case hardened steel, photogravure, motion-picture camera, dial telephone, calcium carbide, Diesel engine, carborundum, motion-picture projector, radio telegraph, electric train control, electric automobile starter, submarine, safety-razor, airplane, flotation process, radio crystal detector, Bakelite, electric-precipitation, gyro-compass, and salvarsan.

"Thirty years of observation and research convince me," says Dr. Grosvenor, "that the proportion of *revolutionary* improvements which is initiated by large corporations is relatively small. I have even seen the lines of progress that were most promising for the

[3] W. M. Grosvenor, The seeds of progress, Chemical Markets, 1929, 24, 23-26.

public benefit, wholly neglected or positively forbidden just because they might revolutionize the industry. We have no right to expect a corporation to cut its own throat from purely eleemosynary motives. Such a thing is contrary to its habit of thought, method of working, and economic policy. It means the obsolescense of all the corporations stand for today. 'A prophet (radical inventor) is not without honor save in his own country (company),' is still true in most cases and quite naturally. Development research, organization, improvements, refinement, great enlargement, economics, broadcast advertising and merchandising—yes, to all these; but to *pioneering*, emphatically no, in most cases. Why should a corporation spend its earnings and deprive its stockholders of dividends to develop something that will upset its own market or junk all its present equipment? Will they make *pioneer* inventions that revolutionize an industry, render present plants and products obsolete? Can corporations be expected to 'hop off' into new horizons of industrial achievement? As well expect an octopus to fly! I have looked up the records to see whether the inventors of a majority of the more or less radical departures (not even wholly pioneering inventions) were employed by a large corporation to work to that end when the invention was made. It appears . . . that the large majority were made by outsiders or were made 'independently' by an officer or director and were either sold to the company or taken elsewhere for development."

We may safely conclude that the majority of the most important inventions and achievements in industry are still being made by the individual inventor, particularly by the "industrial inventor." These men make the wheels of industry go round. They are the officials of the manufacturing companies. We find them also in all the engineering departments of the factories. They may be trained engineers, chemists, machinists, mechanics or superintendents engaged in the engineering work of their factory. A great deal of their work may be pure engineering and designing work which does not fall in the patentable field of invention but any new and non-obvious development of any importance will usually result in being patented. We also find among the "industrial inventors" the man who invents or perfects a device and then manufactures it himself. He may also continue to invent while actively engaged in his manufacturing business, either making improvements or making more inventions in his field. The "industrial inventor" is not necessarily confined to engineering work. He may manufacture toys, various novelties and numerous household and personal appliances. Inventing is not the chief activity of these men; it is only a side-line. However, when it is necessary for them to invent they usually do so in a systematic manner, more or less like the professional inventor.

In view of the importance of the individual inventor, quoting Dr. Grosvenor, "it is vastly important for us to know it and adapt our patent system to give the most perfect protection to the individual, because the nation and the race must rely chiefly on the individual for those great strides of progress, those quick adaptations, which prove its 'fitness to survive.' Then if the large corporations fail to function cooperatively in any particular instance, the outside seeds of progress will not necessarily be neglected or killed; a new corporation can be created to foster it and the old one left to take care of itself."

The assumption underlying our patent statutes that the individual inventor should be encouraged is thus fundamentally sound and the agitation during recent years to correct some of the defects in our patent system so as to adequately encourage the individual inventor is well taken, for he is chiefly responsible for our industrial advances.

CHAPTER IV

The Characteristics of the Inventor

A COMMON concept of the inventor which many people have today is that of an impractical, visionary, long-haired, wild-eyed individual having his head full of new ideas which he thinks will revolutionize the world and make him rich. He is often pictured as a romantic and dreamy figure akin to the poet, a Don Quixote bent on a conquest of the world of matter. The popular concept of the inventor, to put it briefly, is that he is "different" and that he has traits which the normal person does not possess.

In order to determine the actual characteristics of the inventor, the views of patent attorneys who come in close contact with numerous inventors were first obtained. A questionnaire was sent to the most prominent and active patent attorneys in the country. Their views are interesting as well as of some weight. The following two questions, among others, were asked in regard to the characteristics of the inventor: Are inventors different from non-inventors? What are the mental characteristics of the inventor?

In response to the question "Are inventors different from non-inventors?" there were 70 patent attorneys who replied yes, and 106 who replied no. It is thus seen that the majority of the attorneys do not regard the inventor, taken as a class, as having any peculiar traits different from the average person. Many of the patent attorneys pointed out that they have occasionally met some very eccentric "crank inventors" but as a whole they did not find inventors having any traits which would distinguish them from the non-inventor. If inventors have any eccentricities, as it is often stated, then these same eccentricities can probably be found in a similar number of non-inventors.

Inventors differ from non-inventors not on account of any peculiar characteristics, but merely in the nature of their psychological reaction to deficiencies in man's handiwork. The tendency of the non-inventor is to "cuss" deficiencies in his environment, whereas, the bent of the inventor is constructive criticism. He is characterized by the "this-is-the-way-to-do-it" attitude. One of the important characteristics of the inventor is his ability to recognize industrial problems and needs and the possession of native ingenuity in utilizing his bag of tricks in contriving something to satisfy these needs.

One characteristic which perhaps gives most people the idea that inventors are different from other people is the tenacity with which they cling to a problem in the face of apparently insurmountable obstacles. The inventor shows an astonishing persistence of motive and effort. This is likely to give an ordinary person the impression that an inventor is overconfident and even arrogant. Most inventors, of course, strongly believe in their ability and powers. However, in the practical inventor it means merely that he knows that the thing can be done and like the wise man "he knows that he knows" how to do it. Many practical inventors do not consider themselves inventors at all, but merely designers. Their general idea is that they take the knowledge of the ages and combine different elements from this knowledge to perform some desirable end.

The inventor is very often a child of circumstance. A great many people who have the ability to invent have never been in the environment to stimulate their peculiar mental abilities. Others of mediocre talent have simply been able to appreciate the practical importance of more or less accidental discoveries. However, most of us for one reason or another, are potential inventors, and if we fail to invent, we only fail because we lack interest or incentive, or our vocation denies us the opportunity for analysis and original thought. It may be that we are skeptical of our ability to contribute and of the value of our contributions.

The layman, unfamiliar with the history of inventions and the patent systems of the world for protection of inventions, has generally the idea that invention is a haphazard thing, and something which comes suddenly to the inventor, who thereupon patents his idea and reaps large pecuniary benefits. This is entirely erroneous. The average inventor is a man whose early study has fitted him to deal with mechanical, electrical, metallurgical, or chemical developments, and, thereafter devoting himself to the particular industry for which he has studied, he seeks progress and betterment in his particular field. His review of what has been done and his research work leads him to the development of improved methods and devices, and to stimulate growth of his particular subject from small beginnings to a better condition, although he may never hope to reach a complete state. It is probable that if it were not for the stimulus of illegitimate and ill-advised advertising by a few patent attorneys, the granger inventor, who invents one thing in a lifetime and then only because he has been told that letters patent on his invention will bring him a fortune, would entirely disappear. He is in a small minority, as it is, for the greater number of patents taken out are held by large industries, who take them, not with the view of disposing of them, but simply to protect their industry against competition.

Most inventors differ little from non-inventors except in respect to originality. The more prolific inventors ordinarily are simply superior mechanics and engineers of active mind and vision somewhat beyond the usual run of men of the same general class and occupation. Occasionally, one runs across the impractical dreamer but we find this type in all walks of life. Most successful inventors have largely the same characteristics as other successful persons though ordinarily the extreme type, perhaps because of his concentration along his particular line, is often not a good business man.

We have noted in the last chapter that there are several distinct groups of inventors. In each of these groups we are, of course, likely to find the extreme and normal type of inventor. We have noted that the chronic inventor, for example, does nothing else for a living, merely because inventing comes naturally to him. Such inventors are certainly different from non-inventors. They have a mental gift of visionary concepts. They are quick to see a need and just as quick to supply the means for fulfilling that need. Some are so quick at seeing needs that they even invent the need—in other words, pass from the useful to the foolish. Even those inventors fill a useful field because amongst the foolish can be gleaned some good ideas. Chronic inventors will invent anything from a safety-pin to a locomotive, and obtain the impetus by almost any casual remark or by seeing some device which appears to them clumsy, unworkable, impractical or in any way open to improvement. They know the value of an improvement and use inventing as a means of livelihood.

The industrial inventor is the individual who is employed by a manufacturing concern and who conceives of a new way of making something in the business in which he is engaged. This inventor may not be as alert as the chronic inventor and it probably takes him a long time to develop any one invention. This is due to his more or less routine duties and the slow appreciation of some suggestion for improving the product or method with which he is daily engaged. He is usually slow to act and the invention ordinarily is in a high state of perfection before he discloses it to others or files an application for patent. This type of inventor, if in business for himself, makes his invention in the hope of getting a step ahead of his competitors and thus both business rivalry and desire for greater returns compel him to make the invention. As an employee, this type of inventor seeks to make "a hit with the boss" in the hope of getting a "raise," and very few dare to ask for a cash remuneration for the invention. Their purpose originally is to try to prove themselves more valuable and to obtain a wage increase without any expectation of a cash remuneration.

The casual inventor just happens to have seen something that could be improved and is not vocationally interested in seeing it through, nor very likely to derive any cash benefits from the invention. This type of inventor is not likely to appear in the records of the Patent Office more than once in his lifetime.

The replies of 176 patent attorneys to the question "What are the mental characteristics of inventors?" are given in Table 1 which gives the frequencies of the characteristics mentioned.

TABLE 1

FREQUENCY OF CHARACTERISTICS MENTIONED BY 176 PATENT ATTORNEYS

Characteristic	Frequency
Originality	64
Analytic ability	44
Imagination	34
Lack of business ability	26
Perseverance	20
Observation	18
Suspicion	12
Optimism	12
Mechanical ability	6

There were, of course, many other characteristics mentioned but the table gives those which were most frequently given. It will be seen that the first five characteristics emphasized are originality, analysis, imagination, lack of business ability, and perseverence. Next in order came observation, suspicion, optimism, and mechanical ability.

A questionnaire was also sent to the directors of the research and development departments of some of the largest corporations in this country such as DuPont,

General Motors, Radio Corporation, Bell Telephone, General Electric, Goodyear Tire and Rubber Co., etc. They were asked "What are the mental characteristics of research workers and inventors?" The frequencies of the characteristics mentioned are given in the following table.

TABLE 2

FREQUENCY OF CHARACTERISTICS MENTIONED BY 78 DIRECTORS OF RESEARCH

Characteristic	Frequency
Analysis	48
Perseverance	41
Originality	37
Imagination	35
Training and education	20
Reasoning and intelligence	20
Competence	16
Observation	12

It will be observed that analysis, perseverance, originality, and imagination head the list corresponding closely with the order of frequency given by patent attorneys. Training, education, reasoning, confidence, and observation appear next in this table.

An insight into the characteristics of the inventor was obtained from the inventors themselves who were asked in a questionnaire "What are the characteristics of a successful inventor?" Table 3 gives the frequency of the characteristics mentioned by 710 inventors.

TABLE 3

FREQUENCY OF CHARACTERISTICS OF A SUCCESSFUL INVENTOR GIVEN BY 710 INVENTORS

Characteristic	Frequency
Perseverance	503
Imagination	207
Knowledge and memory	183
Business ability	162
Originality	151
Common sense	134
Analytic ability	113
Self-confidence	96
Keen observation	61
Mechanical ability	41

Again, we find that perseverance, imagination, and originality are greatly stressed. A comparison of the three tables shows a very close agreement of the characteristics. Perseverance, originality, and imagination are found among the first five traits given in all three tables. As a whole, there is a good correspondence in the emphasis of the inventor's characteristics. The patent attorneys, for instance, note the frequent lack of business ability in inventions and the inventors stress it as being important for a successful inventor, so that they complement each other.

The frequency of occurrence of the characteristics cannot be taken as a criterion of their importance because the patent attorney, the research director and inventor each regard the question from a different viewpoint. All that we can conclude from these results is that the characteristics noted most frequently are probably of great importance to the inventor. Before these results are further discussed it will be best to give the views of some of the prominent and active inventors in regard to the characteristics of the successful inventor.

ESSENTIALS FOR SUCCESS ACCORDING TO INVENTORS

Dr. Elihu Thomson, who has over 700 patents, states that "the successful inventor should have sound judgment, perseverance, and strict integrity, coupled with the many other qualities. He should have a habit of mind in which obstacles are regarded as things to be overcome, instead of backing down in face of them."

According to Dr. Reginald Fessenden, who has over five hundred patents, the inventor should have "a memory which does not forget, infinite patience, good working knowledge of mathematics, ability to work 18 hours a day for months without tiring."

Another prolific inventor, Dr. Miller Reese Hutchison, who has approximately a thousand patents, stated that the inventor should "see that at which he looks so as to remember it. Hear and comprehend what he is told, remember what he reads, apply the knowledge thus gained in solving problems, forget the clock and abstain from infringing on the ideas of others consciously or otherwise."

The late Emile Berliner has well expressed the qualities an inventor must possess, as follows: "The inventor is privileged to dip into every calling. If he has the right sort of mind it is not at all essential that he understand everything connected with the art with which he desires to make himself familiar. He need only take that particular corner wherein the problem that he is after lies, and work it thoroughly. But thorough the work must be. He must have more than the patience of Job, more than the perseverance of the beaver, more than the industry of the bee. He must work hard, and be content to work for months at a time without making any apparent progress. He must be content to travel over the same field again and again and again, indefatigably. That is the secret of the inventor's success —never-ending application. The idea that an inventor is necessarily a genius is entirely fallacious. Genius for invention is merely the capacity for concentration and for work. Given these qualities and a power of close observation, and you have the make-up of a successful inventor. He need be no learned scientist, and yet he may be able to work up most valuable inventions in many sciences. He need be no perfectly trained electrician, and yet he may be able to work up a valuable electrical appliance. But always he must be prepared to take advantage of new phenomena, and to know all about the field in which they lie. Many of our most important inventions are the result not so much of deep knowledge as of the power of observation and the ability to appreciate the possibilities of phenomena that the less observing would pass by without seeing." [1]

Henry A. Wise Wood, the well-known inventor, has said: "The inventor should avoid falling into the hands of the exploiter. He should avoid taking his eye off the money bags. He should not neglect to so place himself that he can decently support himself and his family. He should not work in one line and invent in another (the whole of his work and thought should be concentrated upon a single objective); he should not let his inventive thoughts wander. If the business he is in gives his inventive faculty no play he should move into a business in which it can be useful. Whatever hardships are involved in changing his line of work when he discovers that it does not satisfy the inventive requirements of his mind he should make a change in the early part of his life. He had best make profitable inventions before he begins having an expensive family. An inventor should not consider an invention made until its practicability is demonstrated by use. He should avoid shyster patent lawyers and should deal only with the best talent obtainable. Any first-class lawyer will temper his charges to the purse of an inventor in whose ability and honesty he believes. If an inventor believes himself to have created a useful thing he should stick to that thing until it goes into use or is proven to be useless, but he must be prepared to undergo whatever hardships, both he and his family, its success requires of him. To be a successful inventor requires in addition to the inventor's faculty, fortitude, industry, patience, self-control, good humor as a lubricant, and an indomitable will. If he desires to own his own inventions he must in addition be shrewd, have a business mind, and a high degree of courage and combativeness. The world has not yet learned that an invention is property in the sense that real estate is, and

[1] Anon., The qualities an inventor must possess, Scientific American, 1902, 86, 242.

therefore does not hesitate to appropriate it if it be not protected."

The following quotations give the views expressed by prominent inventors in regard to the characteristics of the inventor which are essential for success:

"A successful inventor has unlimited patience and the ability to visualize. He knows how to interest capital. Love of work and perseverance in pushing to a conclusion anything undertaken which is worth pushing to a conclusion are important. If to be successful is meant commercial success as measured in financial profits, then the inventor must also be a good executive, as his commercial success will be almost proportionate to his business sagacity and shrewdness."

"Inventors are dissatisfied individuals, that is, in some particular line or group of lines with which they are familiar. They are never satisfied with the old methods employed. They are often unhappy, restless and wish to change things according to their own ideas. An inventor should have a business training and also a sales training to succeed, and be broad minded enough to see both sides."

"He must not be hampered by tradition. He should have a desire to better conditions generally and be willing to work, together with a natural ability to visualize and build something in his mind."

"An inventor must train his mind to eliminate all unessential details and to appreciate any new or old ideas which may come to his observation to the extent that it photographs itself on his mind and may be recalled and worked into a new idea. He should not attempt to cover too wide a field in his inventive work. If the inventor has an idea he should analyze its commercial value from every angle, dependability, and service before wasting his energy, time and money on something which really has no value."

"He must be an idealist who can paint mental pictures of objects that he wishes to produce. He should have in mind that the product is to be of benefit to mankind and indirectly a credit to himself. He must have a resourceful mind with tenacity of purpose."

"Perspicacity and imagination are important. Dream, sleep, eat, your 'art' or your industry. Sanity, clear, straight thinking, close observation and persistency together with good judgment are essential."

"He should have imagination, ability to see errors in present-day devices, and to correct them. An inventor must first have knowledge of what is wanted and then have the ability to carry out the ideas."

"He must be cautious, thorough, have plenty of patience. He must be willing to throw away years of endeavor and research, without regret and completely redesign the idea to fill certain demands. His mind should be rich in association. He should have the ability to perceive, to make discoveries among unrelated concepts, and out of them to create."

"Most important of all I should say is perseverance, and by this I mean staying qualities, the determination to stick to one's idea until it is perfected, after, of course, one has carefully proven to his own satisfaction that his idea is fundamentally practical. One seldom perfects an idea without many failures, and if one is easily discouraged he should not attempt this field of endeavor. Salesmanship I should say would range second, for if one is not fortunate enough to be able to finance his research and development work, one must interest outside capital. This is not easy to do without considerable and too often disastrous sacrifices. Other qualities are as essential to an inventor to be successful as to one in any other kind of business."

"What I consider important is concentration, the ability to perceive a definite object, the ability to analyze the requirements of the problem, and above all the ability to apply to the solution of the problem those simplest mechanical and chemical principles which one has learned throughout years of study and experience."

"I am inclined to place the first qualification of a successful inventor as sound training, the fundamentals of mechanics and other physical sciences; resourcefulness in applying such principles to production of new or better products is, of course, essential. Application and eternal persistence are important factors when combined with pitiless criticism of one's own conceptions and creations. I believe that there is always another way and usually a better one."

"Mechanical judgment and ingenuity make an inventor. A working knowledge in mechanics in a broad sense is sufficient. He must know the gods of the market place and must not get weak-hearted."

"What is important is unlimited persistence, the ability to build something which can be manufactured as well as made in a laboratory; the ability to simplify, the ability to improve on former inventions, the ability to determine manufacturing costs together with the knack of cheap fabrication without the sacrifice of quality. He should be temperate at all times and curb excess imagination."

"The inventor should show discrimination as between the theoretical or the fantastic and practical. He should have perseverance, the ability to withstand discouragement and the ability to demonstrate the value of his invention. A large fund of facts, perception and ability to combine facts to create something new are important."

"He should usually possess at least a fair knowledge of the art and its requirements, have the power to concentrate on the problem at hand and opportunity to put his work to commercial use. Practicability, good memory for mechanical and scientific facts are important. He must be a dreamer, possess spatial imagination, feeling for dynamic and kinetic relations directly rather than through mathematical analysis. He must be a dreamer and not easily daunted by fortune and discouragements. He must feel that the finality has not been reached in anything."

"He should have a general knowledge of the art in which he is working and be possessed of both a constructive and a clear, analytical mind and the determination to attain the objective, and have creative talent, mechanical skill and knowledge of the prior art."

"Patience, health, tenacity of purpose are vital and important. The development of an invention cannot be done on schedule. One cannot work under the time-clock. The days are too short and life, itself, is too short. An inventor should be a draftsman, a mechanic and in possession of the broadest possible knowledge or the ability to find answers to his inquiries."

"A practical and thorough knowledge of what he is about, plenty of patience, willingness to work, and confidence in his ideas are necessary for an inventor."

These remarks and a study of the tables show that perseverance is the trait most emphasized by the inventors. Undoubtedly this is a very important characteristic. It is easy to conceive and develop an invention mentally, but it is another matter to actually complete the invention in material and tangible form. Many difficulties and unforeseen problems arise as soon as the inventor begins to embody his invention in terms of gears, pulleys, and levers. Days and months of hard work may be necessary before he perfects the invention from its first crude conception. The inventor must be persistent in his efforts. He must be willing to give up years of work and to begin over again. This requires infinite patience, courage, and determination. The inventor cannot be slipshod and haphazard. He must work systematically and thoroughly. He perseveres unremittingly in spite of his own failures and obstacles as well as those of others who worked before him. Perseverance requires great will-power and concentration, and the ability to bob up after discouragement with the hope of a new solution. It demands a great deal of sacrifice and a strong constitution and health. We all know how Edison worked for weeks in his laboratory both day and night with only a few hours sleep before he perfected the incandescent electric lamp. He showed heroic patience and profound perseverance. This quality is necessary for all inventors if they are to succeed. Eight hours a day, five days a week will never make a man an inventor.

After the invention is perfected to his satisfaction the inventor must convince the public of its value. He must fight the apathy and indifference and overcome the mental inertia which he will find everywhere toward his invention until he wins over the public and gains its confidence. The path of the inventor is at best rough and thorny. He battles with many odds against him. He must keep up his optimism and courage while fighting the obstinate world of matter as well as his indifferent and conservative fellow-men.

Everyone will agree that originality is the distinct characteristic of the inventor for he is essentially creative. He possesses the capacity of seeing non-obvious things. This is the most important faculty of the inventor, for if all inventive development were obvious, civilization would have been perfected long ago.

The inventor can conceive things which he has never seen and which have never existed. He takes the known and old ideas and creates new and non-obvious patterns out of them. The inventor has that rare ability by which he can see, read and absorb the ideas of others without allowing them to influence his own thoughts, except in a minor and entirely secondary way.

He must possess an ingenious mind and be able to visualize and imagine conditions and objects and associate them in a practical way. He is a man of original thoughts and constitutionally averse to blindly following the old way of doing things. Custom does not always represent the best way to carry on. The inventor questions any method of accomplishing a result or any piece of mechanism that for a long period has been accepted as good enough. Any practice that has been long continued frequently represents a rich field for the ingenious thinker. To be told that "his ideas were tried out years ago and were found to be no good" does not necessarily discourage him. The inventor never acquiesces to tradition. He is not conventional but rather an innovator and leader. He is unhappy with things as they are and wants to change them. He is a non-conformist. He is dissatisfied with what he finds and wants to improve things. He has a strong desire to alter and to change.

He persuades himself to look at old ideas with a new outlook and to pretend he is looking at them for the first time in his life and to criticize them accordingly. To accomplish what he desires the inventor must have originality, vision, perseverance, and logic. Originality to enable him to progress on a project. Vision to enable him to see where the project is leading him. Perseverance to keep him from becoming discouraged even though his work shows an apparent lack of correlation between variables he is considering. Logic to enable him to progress in his work by means of correct reasoning as to the meaning of his experimental data. But in addition he must be ingenious, versatile and resourceful. When one method fails he resorts by means of his ingenuity and resourcefulness to new methods. His versatility suggests new roads to travel which would not occur to the average person. It is only in this manner that he can create.

Imagination is another characteristic which has been stressed by the inventors as being important. We shall not attempt here to discuss the psychological significance and meaning of imagination as this will be done in Chapter VI. Without imagination it would be difficult, if not impossible to invent. By means of his imagination the inventor re-arranges known ideas into new combinations. He takes the facts of his past experience and forms new patterns from them. However, he must have a restrainable imagination which takes account of facts and is subordinated to them. Imagination has been regarded to be so important by some, that they have gone so far as to define invention as imagination. However, it is not the imagination of the fairy-tale that is meant but a practical, constructive and controlled imagination. The inventor must be able to visualize and imagine conditions and objects and have the ability to associate these in a practicable application.

Together with imagination we sometimes find an interesting streak of the artistic and poetic temperament in inventors. Many important inventions have been actually made by artists. Morse, the inventor of the telegraph, was a landscape painter. He was also the president of the National Academy of Design for many years. Fulton, who is famed for his steamboat, was a portrait painter. Arkwright, the inventor of the spinning-frame, wrote verses. Watt was a rhymer in his youth. Cartwright, the inventor of the power-loom, also wrote poetry. Da Vinci was a remarkable artist as well as an inventor. Mechanical invention and other forms of art have a common characteristic which is the visualization of their creations. The artist and the inventor only differ in the physical medium which they use for their expression. The artist works on a flat canvas. The sculptor and architect work in a world of three dimensions, and the inventor adds the feature of motion. With the addition of motion many new problems arise which limit the freedom of the inventor's expression. Another similarity between the artist and inventor is that the inventor must always keep his eye on the practical aspect of his creation. This is in a sense also true of the artist, for if he does not adhere to the world of truth his art fails and lacks conviction.

In order to supply the materials for the imagination to utilize, the inventor must have a keen sense of observation and a retentive memory. By remembering he can often use an old idea in a new way. Many important inventions can be attributed to accident but the accident alone is not sufficient to produce the invention. The inventor must be there to observe and take note of what happens. He must be able to understand the significance of the accidental phenomenon and realize its utility. However, before all this can happen he must first observe and observe well.

Let us take, for instance, the invention of the bridge. No doubt primitive man saw thousands upon thousands of times fallen tree trunks across streams. But when the inventor came he did not merely observe the fallen tree trunk. He saw something more. He saw the fallen tree in a new relation or pattern which could serve for a useful and predetermined purpose.

The importance of observation and insight is illustrated by the following story of an inventor, B. W. Coltman, who developed a new process of making light, airy soap chips. One day, as he lathered his face with soap preparatory to shaving, he happened to notice an interesting item in a newspaper. He began to read, and became so interested that he forgot about his shave so that the soap dried on his face. As he proceeded to remove the dried soap he observed that it formed light, airy chips and it occurred to him that here was a method for making a new kind of soap chips. An apparatus was finally developed by him for dissolving and aerating soap, drying it on a belt and forming soap chips similar to those he found on his face. Thus we see that the inventor must be alert, wide-awake and observe everything with an analytic and keen mind.

It is, of course, essential for the inventor to have a thorough knowledge of the fundamental principles of science as well as the major facts of his particular field in order to understand modern technical problems. If he is to make any useful inventions in his field he must be acquainted with the peculiar problems involved and the available means to solve them which are feasible and practicable commercially. Many important inventions have been formerly made by "outsiders," that is, by men who were utter strangers in the field. But as our technical and scientific knowledge increases and more and more inventions are made it will become increasingly necessary for the future inventor to have a thorough technical knowledge and training.

Clear thinking and reasoning have also been considerably stressed by inventors as well as by research directors. Inventors as a group are probably more intelligent than the non-inventors. If inventors have the characteristics and qualities previously mentioned they must necessarily be highly intelligent. The characteristics mentioned are, of course, essential to success in any field of human endeavor, but the inventor is differentiated by the way he utilizes these human traits, qualitatively as well as quantitatively. The inventor must have plenty of common sense and good judgment in order to properly direct his activities. The entire process of invention is really an indication of intelligence. Certainly the idiots and feeble-minded do not invent. All the perseverance, creative ability and imagination in the world would not amount to anything unless the inventor used his sound judgment and keen intellect in selecting his problem, eliminating non-essentials, planning the method of attack and modifying his plans as he goes along to suit conditions and circumstances as they arise.

The ability to analyze is really one phase of intelligence. It is probably highly important for developing any invention. The inventor is enabled by his ability to analyze and by his judgment to readily separate the "wheat from the chaff" of his mental suggestions. It is important that the analysis be quantitative as well as qualitative, as the success or failure of a thing often depends, not only on how big it has to be, or how it is to be proportioned in its parts, but also whether it will work or not in principle. Here is the place where many inventors fall down, and a great amount of money is wasted, because they do not have the mental ability or persistence to analyze the details of their problem quantitatively. The inventor must be honest to himself and be ready to be his own most severe critic. He should always be evaluating suggested ways and means and eliminate all undesirable attempts by critical analysis.

A successful inventor is more shrewd than the average individual, both in observing the necessity for a non-existent device and in analyzing all the possible methods of supplying it. He is quick to perceive a demand or need, which may actually exist or which may be only latent. Very often he is much ahead of his time especially when the need is latent. Years may pass before his invention is actually used before the conditions which he perceived and analyzed actually materialize. The commercial success of an invention is often dependent upon its timeliness rather than upon its intrinsic worth.

In order to achieve any objective, especially in untrodden fields, self-confidence is absolutely essential. This trait is important for the inventor. He must believe in his own powers and rely on them unhesitatingly. He is persistent in his work in spite of his failures because he has faith and confidence in his ability to eventually overcome the difficulty. The inventor is, therefore, courageous and optimistic. His energy never flags. He often bubbles over with enthusiasm because he visualizes his inventions and seldom doubts that he will not achieve his aim.

A great deal has been said about the inventor as a business man. About 25 per cent of the inventors stressed the fact that the successful inventor must have business ability. It is one thing to make an invention and quite another thing to commercialize it. In order to reap the benefits of his work, the inventor must be able to interest capital to finance him, so that he may manufacture his invention, or, if he sells his invention outright, he must have sufficient business sagacity and acumen to drive a good bargain. Of course, if the inventor is employed to invent he has no business difficulties to negotiate. He merely receives his salary and devotes his entire energies to inventing.

There seems to be a general concensus among inventors that inventing as a whole does not pay. It is difficult to tell whether this is due to their lack of business ability or to other causes. For one thing, our patent laws do not adequately protect or reward the inventor. An inventor who makes a financial success of his invention today must, therefore, have a great deal of business ability to reap his rewards.

It is interesting to note that mechanical ability has not been stressed very much either by inventors or patent attorneys. In these days of high mechanical perfection almost any mechanism can be made to order. The inventor, therefore, need not have actual mechanical ability. What he must have is a mechanical sense and a thorough knowledge of mechanism. The inventor need not necessarily be a builder. He can have his machines built for him. It would be interesting to know how much mechanical aptitude is actually possessed by inventors. Many inventors, of course, are excellent workers with their hands. In the great industrial organizations, however, we often have inventors who never even touch a screw-driver. The complete invention is built by skilled workers and mechanics under his direction and supervision.

Practically all the inventors of the study were intensely interested in mechanical things when they were young. Undoubtedly this early interest in mechanical devices has been a potent factor in their later activity as serious inventors. The familiarity and experience gained by manipulation of mechanical contrivances in early boyhood gave them a definitely favorable mental attitude toward mechanism. This is extremely valuable to them as inventors, for it enables them to think in terms of their past kinesthetic experiences and it helps them to visualize their inventions before they are actually constructed in physical form.

No attempt has been made in this chapter to evaluate the psychological significance of the characteristics noted except in a casual manner. The purpose has been merely to enumerate and discuss the most frequently noted traits of the inventor in order to lay a foundation for their discussion on a psychological basis in later chapters.

CHAPTER V

ACTUAL METHODS OF INVENTING

THE ideal method to determine the actual steps taken by an inventor in making an invention would be to place him in a psychological laboratory so as to observe him at his work. There are, however, several serious difficulties involved in this method. First of all, the inventive process often extends over a long period of time, and it is not always on tap. It is not entirely under the control of the inventor who often has to wait for the favorable moment and the period of so-called inspiration which may take weeks or even years to occur. Another difficulty is that the inventive process is seldom continuous and uninterrupted. The inventor often works in irregular spurts of effort and activity. A still more serious objection is that if we should put the inventor at work in a laboratory we are removing him from his normal setting and environment. All the incentives to invent may disappear under such artificial conditions.

Even assuming that these difficulties were obviated we would next have the utmost difficulty of obtaining the consent of active inventors to come to our psychological laboratory. Inventors, especially of the type that we are interested in, are extremely busy men. They have many pressing problems and duties on their hands which would prevent them from participating in such experimental studies.

The other alternative, therefore, would be to question the inventors and ask them to state what methods they follow in inventing. This was actually done by means of a questionnaire. We must remember that we are dealing with an extremely active group of inventors who have obtained on the average 39.3 patents. It is, therefore, obvious that what these men have to say will shed a great deal of light on our problems.

A careful analysis of the replies of 710 inventors reduces the procedure in inventing to the following distinct steps:

1. Observation of a need or difficulty
2. Analysis of the need
3. A survey of all available information
4. A formulation of all objective solutions
5. A critical analysis of these solutions for their advantages and disadvantages
6. The birth of the new idea—the invention
7. Experimentation to test out the most promising solution, and the selection and perfection of the final embodiment by some or all of the previous steps.

The first and most essential step in the process of invention is the clear recognition of a new, latent, or incompletely satisfied need or difficulty. It is this definite recognition of a want which is the spark that initiates the entire inventive activity of the inventor. The persistence and the effort which are expended in meeting this want, until it is met or satisfied, depend on the incentives which urge the inventor to produce and create. This is a matter which will be discussed separately in Chapter X. For the present, we are not interested in the motives or incentives of the inventor and we shall assume that they are present so as to cause him to go through the entire inventive process to its completion so as to produce a practical and successful invention.

The experience of a want and the striving to satisfy this want probably constitute the basis of all human activity and the inventive process is merely a special phase of this fundamental activity in a more acute form. Our inventions today aim to satisfy fundamental human wants or to meet the needs created by existing inventions. An inventor may, therefore, study new physical and chemical principles in order to apply them in a useful form to satisfy human wants or he may study the inventions which are already in use in the industries in order to improve them so as to better satisfy our wants. The great majority of the inventions made today are of the latter class and it is with this class of inventions that the inventors of this study are chiefly engaged.

The observation of a need or difficulty often comes after a careful study and analysis of existing apparatus, processes or conditions on the part of the inventor with the object of seeing how they could be improved, either by radical changes or by improving certain parts of the apparatus or process. This occurs frequently in the regular course of his every day work. The inventor is ever on the alert to observe shortcomings and defects. He may notice that the devices before him are crude, costly and inefficient. The machinery may be weak in certain places and faulty in operation. The inventor may also study a highly competitive or even a neglected or backward field which seems to have possibilities for development. In other words, the inventor is a careful and keen observer who is on the alert to note defects or needs, whether they are obvious and apparent, or dormant and not particularly apparent.

A problem or difficulty may also be called to his attention by others in the course of his business. Someone may suggest a problem, which defies solution, or his attention may be called to an unsatisfied need by a casual remark or by reading an article.

The next important step consists in a thorough analysis and study of the result to be obtained which has been perceived or noted by any of the methods just explained. Nearly all the inventors stress that it is highly important not only to perceive the need but also to have a clear idea of the object in view. Some inventors stated that in order to clarify their objectives they put their thoughts in writing and state as clearly as possible just what they want to accomplish. The inventor must, therefore, first observe carefully and then he must analyze what he observes, eliminate all irrelevant and non-essential details and clearly formulate the essential elements of his problem before he can proceed further. He must ask himself just what he proposes to do. His object may be to simplify a known machine or process, increase the efficiency of operation, reduce the expense of manufacture, lessen the number of operations on a machine, permit the automatic operation of a machine, prevent loss of life and property.

The third step of the inventive process followed by nearly all the inventors of this study consists in a survey of all available information bearing on the problem at hand. This may include a careful search through the technical literature and patents. All the existing methods are carefully studied. There also may be discussions and conferences with experts, associates, workmen, producers, and buyers until all available information is obtained on the particular problem. There are some few inventors who deliberately omit this step fearing that this information will cause them to follow the old methods and prevent them from regarding the problem with a fresh and original outlook. Most of the inventors, however, who make a thorough survey of a particular field are able to mentally brush aside the old methods and combinations and remain entirely uninfluenced by this information in devising their own solutions. The information merely provides them with ideas or mental elements which are employed in the inventive process to make new combinations.

The next step consists in devising and formulating "objective solutions," that is, all possible ways and means to satisfy the need, utilizing all the known available means obtained by the preceding step. These objective solutions include those that are known to the inventor or which can be devised without necessitating a wholly new conception. Such solutions will ordinarily occur to those who are well versed in their specific field without involving invention of a very high order.

We shall now assume that the inventor has visualized in his mind or sketched on paper all the possible solutions. His fifth step consists in a critical analysis of these solutions for their advantages and disadvantages. This involves logic, judgment, and good reasoning. The different components of each solution may be separated and examined separately depending on the character of the invention. The possibility and feasibility of developing the necessary mechanism must be examined. A rigid examination of the economic and commercial requirements must be made. Many of the possible solutions will thus be eliminated at once. Is the proposed solution more efficient than the existing devices? Is it original? Has it been suggested by others? Will it accomplish all the objects which were set out to be accomplished? An analysis must be made of the upkeep of the proposed invention, its cost of manufacture and its operation. It must, to put it briefly, comply with all the fundamental engineering and commercial requirements. The proposed solution must make profits, it must meet competition effectively and there must be a commercial demand for it. It must accomplish the result by the shortest and simplest method. The practical operating conditions of the device must be considered in order to see whether it will satisfy actual working conditions. The parts must be strong, simple, easily replaced or repaired at a minimum of expense and they must be able to withstand long and hard usage.

Henry Ford is quoted in this connection to say: "Is it needed? Is it practical? Is it commercial? These all go together; they are sound and honest tests; if they are abused at all it is usually by those who have failed to pass them. The fulfillment of human need is the great success. To do this, the method or instrument proposed must be practical—that is, it must be usable. And then to get it abroad into use, it must be commercialized, which means, put within reach of all who need it. These are life's own tests; to know them may prevent mistakes."

Many of these questions and requirements can be answered by cold analysis and reasoning. However, they must ultimately be tested out physically.

At this point, after the problem has been dealt with objectively and still is unsolved, a new idea flashes upon the mind, a new pattern suddenly appears, a new relationship is seen. It is the new idea, the conception that is greater than the sum of the parts that have entered into it, which is the invention. This step is principally a mental process often culminating in the visualization of the solution. It is here that the inventor's imagination and the so-called "inventive or creative faculty" have full and free play. A great number of the inventors sketch their solutions as fast as they come without regard to their practicability. This process may occur at almost any time. It is the period of the so-called "inspirations." They may come at any hour and at any place. One inventor states that he gets his best flashes when he is alone in the bathroom. Another inventor gets his ideas at the theatre or during a sermon. Others awake in the early morning hours with a clear solution. It is a period of mental ferment and unrest, and whatever the psychological processes may be, the inventor is finally aware of one or more possible solutions. This process may take a few minutes or it may take years, and it is probably for this reason that the inventive processes will never be studied in the laboratory. In this step of his inventive process an obscure and little understood mental process appears to be going on which takes all the known elements of his past experience and recombines them in a new way to meet the problem he is trying to solve. The psychological aspects of this process will be fully discussed in the next chapter.

Having obtained a promising solution by the foregoing steps, the seventh step in the inventive process consists in experimentation to test out the tentative solution which appears to have most advantages and the fewest disadvantages by embodying it in physical form and actually determining whether it fulfills the particular requirements. The building and testing of the least expensive and most promising design will often reveal unsuspected faults and defects. Undesirable and cumbersome features may be eliminated. The mechanism may be simplified and redesigned so as to meet the commercial requirements. The final result is thus often entirely different in form from the first conception except that it may embody its original principles. Actual experiment may often show that the proposed solutions are unsuccessful. A careful study and analysis of the unsuccessful device must then be made in order to determine the reasons for its failure. New facts or principles may thus be discovered and the entire inventive process must then be repeated until a successful invention is produced. It is in this experimental stage that a great deal of trial and error procedure must be followed. The inventor must be persistent and patient. He must be willing to spend months and years in hard work trying again and again newly formulated solutions. Accidental discoveries may result and unexpected solutions may be made. On the whole, however, the experimental stage involves a rigid and logical procedure and hard work.

Several methods may be used in the experimental stage depending on the nature of the device and the experience of the inventor. He may make a rough model in wood or other cheap material in order to determine the practicability of the invention. When some specific features are in question, each may be made separately and then combined in the whole machine. Sometimes the entire machine is built from carefully calculated and dimensioned drawings. It is not essential that the inventor himself be an expert machinist or technician. He may have the models made by engineers or mechanics.

We can readily understand why many of our inventions were made empirically. Many of the essential facts and principles necessary to complete the invention were unknown. The inventor had no available scientific or technical knowledge to help him. He was, therefore, forced to find the missing element by a cut and try method, following no logical or definite method. The inventor in early times was, therefore, often forced to be a discoverer in order to find the necessary elements to meet his need. For this reason nearly all basic inventions involve an element of discovery which may be the ascertainment of some fact or the recognition of a new relationship. Modern inventions, however, are chiefly improvement inventions. The inventor usually has at his command all the necessary elements for his invention. He is seldom forced to find new ones and his chief work is to use the known elements by recombining them into new patterns to satisfy his needs.

The steps in this inventive process which have been outlined are taken consciously or unconsciously by most inventors. The failure or success of any inventor depends upon the thoroughness with which he takes each step. There is, of course, no sharp and rigid demarcation of each step. The observations, the mental processes, the analyses and experiments may blend and fuse into each other. As the inventor is experimenting he may be analyzing, making observations and devising new ways of solving the need before him. Many of the steps may be going on simultaneously, but on the whole they follow the order of steps outlined rather closely, according to the statements of the inventors themselves.

An excellent example illustrating the process of invention is given by the following description in making an invention by William H. Smyth, of Berkeley, Cal., inventor, and author of "Concerning Irascible Strong."

"The problem to be solved, or . . . the want to be satisfied, relates to means adapted to solder both ends simultaneously on fruit cans in the time previously required for one end. The mental material available for the solution of the problem consisted of a somewhat extensive acquaintance with mechanical devices generally, and a limited one with the state of the art relating to soldering devices.

"As the mechanisms for handling the cans are not necessary to the illustration, it may be assumed that they were of a character to suitably feed and discharge cans in the varying conditions under which the solder was applied. They will, therefore, be no more particularly referred to.

"The state of the art before spoken of embraced solder in bulk, bars, rods and wire; hand tools, such as soldering irons of various forms and furnaces of different kinds for heating them, adapted to use solid, fluid and gaseous fuel (Fig. 2). It also included fluid solder in open troughs, i. e., solder baths through which, for the purpose of applying solder, cans were caused to roll in an inclined position, dipping the cover joint beneath the solder surface.

"The first procedure was, of course, a survey of the material. This immediately disclosed two distinct lines of possible devices, one based upon the employment of solid solder, and the other upon the use of the fluid solder bath; rapidity and simplicity, two extremely desirable qualities, are presented by the bath; consequently its possibilities received thorough consideration, resulting in two equally unpromising alternatives. The first of these involves bending the can so that its opposite ends may dip simultaneously in the solder, as in Figure 1, and the second, bending the fluid up to meet the ends of the can, as in Figure 3.

"These alternatives proved so extremely unpromising that consideration turned to the solid solder devices. In this direction the problem, in its essence, means a duplication of hand tools (Fig. 4) operated and fed automatically. So the device assumed the form shown in Figure 5

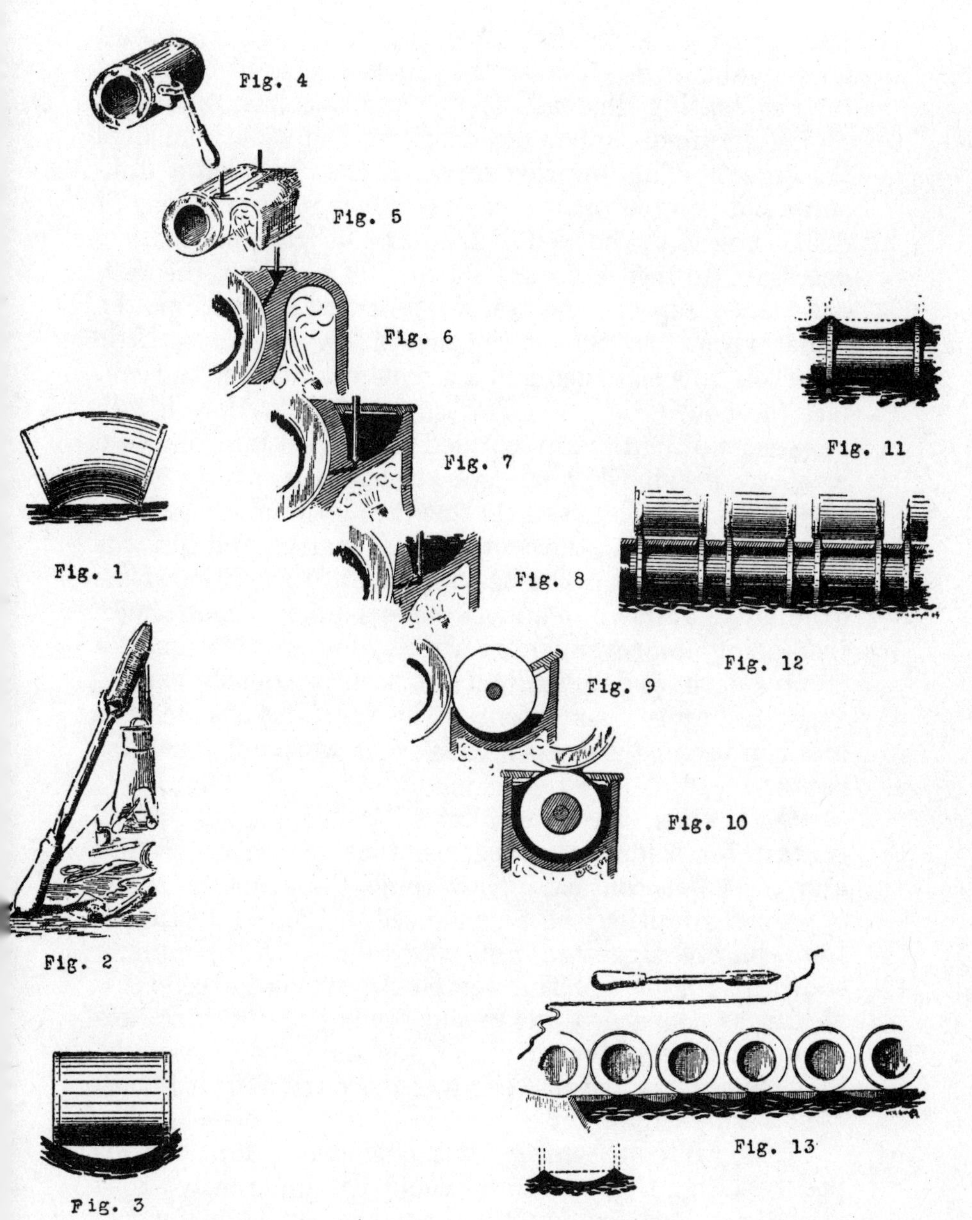

Steps in devising a can soldering machine.

with gratifying results, excepting only that the solder wire would, at times, leave the groove prepared for it.

"Perforating, instead of grooving, the iron, and supplying a funnel-shaped cup to direct the wire, remedied the defect. This improvement not only avoided a difficulty, but pointed in an unmistakable manner to a way of dispensing with the complicated and delicate mechanism necessary to feed the wire solder. In practice, the funnel-shaped cup became a miniature reservoir of molten solder (Fig. 6). So for the reason suggested, the little reservoir was enlarged and a simple valve added to regulate the flow (Fig. 7). This slight modification, it will be seen, unintentionally carried the device into the fluid category, previously abandoned as hopeless.

"It was now observed that owing to the much greater heat of fluid solder, the contact between iron and can was entirely too large. The bearing surface was, therefore, gradually cut down to almost mere contact (Fig. 8) with increasing improvement in result; but at this stage a trouble developed which had not been previously experienced to any serious extent. The friction between iron and can became a factor. The irons wore out much too rapidly.

"Here, then, was a conflict of requirements. Small contact for soldering—large surface for wear—in one and the same contact. How could these diametrically opposing conditions be harmonized? Rolling contact is immediately suggested, and was adopted in the manner shown in Figure 9. This served the purpose excellently, so far as concerned wear; but, owing to the large exposure of the soldering wheel, too much heat was lost. So what was gained in wear was more than offset by loss of soldering capability.

"However, the remedy was obvious—reduce the exposure (Fig. 10). Nothing could be, apparently, more simple and satisfactory, for the device is now in form to solder simultaneously, not only both ends of one can, but both ends of a practically unlimited number. A further advantage is incidentally achieved in that the cans, by rotating the solder discs, control their own solder feed. It is interesting to notice at this point also that the seemingly paradoxical feat of causing the solder surface to bend upward to meet the ends of a horizontal can is accomplished (Figs. 11 and 12).

"Up to this stage the cans are soldered in batches, the units of which must be fed and discharged simultaneously. The question is naturally suggested, could the same results be obtained upon cans fed in a continuous stream? This accomplished, the wished-for goal is reached, though by a somewhat unexpected way.

"To those who have carefully followed the solution thus far, the necessary change will offer little difficulty. It is, in fact, almost obtrusively apparent, needing but one stroke of a pen to the sketch represented in Figure 13. Discs are dispensed with and the conflicting requirements which suggested them are even more perfectly harmonised in the later construction.

"Assuming, then, the last step taken, a device appears which applies solder to both ends, simultaneously, of each unit of a continuous stream of cans, rolling in single file upon horizontal axes above a horizontal surface of solder." [1]

The apparatus described here has actually been patented by W. H. Smyth in U. S. patents No. 573,423, December 15, 1896 and 659,381 October 9, 1900.

REMARKS OF INVENTORS ON HOW TO INVENT

A few of the typical replies of the inventors will now be given in order to illustrate concretely the methods which they follow in inventing. These statements embody the wisdom gained through years of experience and the expenditure of vast fortunes. Anyone interested in inventing will obtain by carefully reading these re-

[1] W. H. Smyth, Is the inventive faculty a myth? Cassier's Magazine, 1897, 12, 676-683.

marks valuable information which has never been published before.

"In inventing, the first step is to ascertain what type of invention is needed to fill a certain need. Comparable devices are then studied. The general requirements are then kept in mind until I have what might be called an inspiration which I may get at any time and at any place. I carry with me at all times a pad for putting down these ideas which are then gone over more carefully, usually being worked up so that an experimental device is manufactured before the patent is applied for." (R. S. Bassett)

"Find out as far as possible what every one has said and done in any way related to the subject, carefully noting distinction between verified facts, guesses, and opinions. Learn physics, chemistry, mathematics, as they may have a possible bearing on the problem. Frequently important information at first seems very remote from the problem. Then create mental images of the device, assisted by sketches and so on, until one seems satisfactory. Finally build it and see how good a mental image was made. Of course these steps are usually taken in part and very much mixed up during the perfection of an invention." (Frederick K. Blue)

"During the last thirty years, my inventions have been inspired by the need for doing things that could not be accomplished by means available. Investigate prior art, try to think of the greatest possibility for simplicity, and there naturally follow large numbers of experiments; first to discover as many solutions as possible, second, to try out or demonstrate the solutions; third, to refine and mature the solution that is thought to be most practicable." (S. L. Cluett)

"When working out a new device, mental pictures present themselves to my mind quite rapidly, more rapidly in fact than I can record them on paper. Therefore, the first step seems to be a process of eliminating the imaginary pictures to reduce the group to those most feasible. Another process of elimination follows after making free-hand sketches, and a further process of elimination follows after laying the parts out to scale and studying the functions of the different parts in detail. This usually brings me to a lay-out (in complicated cases) which requires reinventing, or at any rate additional scheming in order to improve some of the objections or phases of the mechanism." (A. Y. Dodge)

"Casual invention may come from imagination, visualization and perseverance. Repetitive invention, which after all is the thing that we are most concerned with, has always been preceded by prolonged analysis. During this analytical period there is direct contact with and observation of the process, apparatus or product desired to be improved or duplicated by another method, this contact and observation resulting in sharp mental pictures or units, has been essential. It is with these sharp images that a number of new pictures are synthesized and reconstructed just as a child builds up a number of buildings with blocks. These imaginary processes, apparatus or materials are then subjected to a series of destructive hypotheses. A limited number are not blown or knocked down. Of this limited number the one that seems to have the most resistance to destructive hypotheses is given physical embodiment, as nearly as this can be done in the laboratory, and subjected to real and not hypothetical destructive forces. If it stands the test, which none ever do without some modification, it is passed on to the semi-works scale where it must again resist destructive tests. A more severe test then comes when this, now always very seriously modified, semi-works physical embodiment of the inventive idea is analyzed to determine whether it can be again embodied on the large scale and in the engineering materials available for commercial operation." (F. G. Breyer)

"I have no set rules or procedure in my inventing. Generally speaking I am led to improve devices with which I am somewhat familiar, due to defects which I see either in their construction or operation. In designing a product I always seek to simplify, keeping in mind the requirements for economic manufacture, as well as ease of installation or operation. Ideas often occur to me without conscious effort or concentration. It appears to be on the order of inspiration, usually when I am rested, and allow my mind to wander at will. I often prefer to attack a problem without knowing the previous patent or commercial art, and thus avoid following beaten paths. I have been criticized for this method by those who study the situation first of all from the standpoint of past history, and then try to find some other way of accomplishing the purpose, but this is not usually my method. I prefer to have my mind free for any ideas that may come to me without being burdened with visions of past performances. In other cases I take what I consider to be the best known design for a given purpose, and study that design with the idea of improvement, trying to eliminate any but necessary parts, or to overcome known or apparent defects.

"After I have completed a design I usually have a model made so as to more clearly visualize the device, and eliminate by further designing any imperfections that appear. In some cases several models are made before I am satisfied with the device, and very often have to discard the invention as being impractical, or not of sufficient value to carry further. I usually do not consider seriously the matter of my invention infringing other patents until after I have perfected the device and know what it consists of, and then if thought advisable look into the question of infringement or await the Patent Office actions to determine what the prior art may be. The inventor should avoid wasting his time on devices or improvements for which there would be a limited sale, or for which there would be a good deal of sales resistance, for after he has developed a device of this character he would find it extremely difficult to get anyone to manufacture and sell it.

"In designing a device for a given purpose the use to which it is to be put should be very carefully considered as a guide in the design. Simplicity should always be sought, and if it is a device requiring various forms the matter of standardization should be kept clearly in mind, and as far as practical interchangeability of parts. The knowledge of materials best suited is essential, for the materials to be used oftentimes determine the character of the design." (R. B. Benjamin)

"My own inventions have almost without exception been concerned with my own business or profession or with contacts that came as a result of such business. I try to first get a picture of the situation that an invention applies to and try to determine the usefulness or the demand for this invention. In many cases specific problems have been put to me by others to solve and that started the particular invention.

"The next step is to give a great deal of thought to the picture and try to see how the invention will fit in with this picture, analyzing the whole situation carefully and attempting to get the fundamental points involved. The next thing is to determine just what can be done to solve the particular problem. This is the strictly inventor's part of it, to find the key which unlocks the situation. That seems to call upon some special aptitude, and probably most people are utterly unable to furnish anything in this stage of the game.

"How the idea comes to any inventor—whether the idea is good or poor, or whether the inventor is a little man or a big man—is puzzling. Usually in my case it has seemed to 'pop' out of the air, and the air seems to be full of these things but they will not 'pop' until you do something requiring extreme mental concentration. I have had so many ideas come at eleventh hours in critical places, where they just simply had to come. The ideas often come after a night's sleep and do not appear to have been conscious thoughts. My own belief is that they are certain combinations which have been drawn from past experience and rolled together in some manner in the brain without any conscious process on the part of the inventor.

"If this key stage or strictly conception stage of invention is passed, then the invention is under way, and my practice is to immediately draw up a sketch and a written description of the invention—if it cannot be at that time worked out in any detail, at least a diagrammatic idea is worked out.

"Following this, of course, is the usual stereotyped procedure. It depends, of course, upon what the invention relates to. It is put through the research departments and the scientist, the physicist and the chemist get to work upon the detailed things that are involved; the designer and the engineer, in case of a machine, are called in to begin the assembly of a practical unit which later goes through the fabrication period where the experimental machine is usually built, then come periods of trial and experiment, the successful results of which give the data that produce the successful complete commercial machine." (G. E. Howard)

"I endeavor to get a complete understanding of the problem. I also usually have a search made to learn the state of the prior art. Sometimes valuable suggestions can be obtained from previous patents, and this enables one to avoid re-inventing something that has already been patented.

"I find it valuable to try to think of doing something in an opposite or different way from that in which it usually has been done before. Even though the first suggestion or thought may be quite impractical, it usually leads to other thoughts or combinations which may be the germ of a new idea.

"I usually make a list in the order of their importance of all devices which I think might accomplish the result. I study each one independently and eliminate those which further study shows may be impractical." (E. C. Loetscher)

"The first step is to conceive a need or use, examining the existing art or processes or to imagine (visualize) a desirable something or process which might respond to or create a demand. Another phase is to have presented an existing demand requiring the solution of a problem. An inventor must be something of a skeptic as to the perfectness of existing devices or processes, believing in unlimited future improvement or development. This involves wide reading, understanding of principles, etc. Then follows the work of the imagination (creative imagination) which involves the ability to picture to one's mind the device or process as if it were already in existence. In this mental picture the invention is embodied, even tested, so to speak. A verdict must now be arrived at as to the operativeness of the plans and possible value in achievement (not necessarily in a financial sense). After all, I have found the greater joy to be that of achievement—a problem solved.

"It is scarcely necessary to add that I regard the imaginative faculty as chief in value to the inventor, as it is to the work of the constructing engineer, the artist, the architect, the researcher, etc. I have never tried by chance or numerous experiments to reach the goal, and consequently have never begun a piece of work, invention included, in which I could not in my mind follow the whole thing through to an apparently satisfactory conclusion." (Dr. Elihu Thomson)

"From broad general business contacts, I ascertain the economic need for a new product, or a new method of making an old product. I study carefully the limitations of present methods of accomplishing the result with particular reference to the applicability of new materials or new ways of using old materials. The possibility of using new materials or new methods is determined by experiments illustrating the essential points of the invention. A machine is built, preferably a full-size machine, but not necessarily the largest commercial machine. Difficulties of design, materials, or operation, are fought through point by point until the machine evolves itself into a well-operating commercial device. Depending upon the particular circumstances of the case, patent applications are filed and commercial exploitation takes place during any of the above steps." (C. Field)

"The inventions with which I have been concerned might be classified in two parts. The first of these concerns doing something which has not yet been accomplished, and for which a need appears to exist. In this case one mentally musters all the available tools and means for arriving at the desired end, and seeks that means, or what is most likely, a combination of means, which will accomplish the desired result. The second general procedure is to learn of some new physical idea or set of facts which may have been arrived at by pure research processes by someone else, and to scan mentally the various practical things whose accomplishment may be aided by the employment of the new physical tool. The latter process may often result in an invention which has nothing to do with the particular line of work in which I may be engaged at the instant." (H. A. Affel)

"First, I am inclined to avoid extensive reading about inventions which have been made by others in the particular art in which I am especially interested. This is for the purpose of escaping prejudice or suggestions which might unconsciously bias my action. After having decided what I would like to accomplish I analyze and try to work out the problem in my mind. Conditions are much more favorable for me to do this out in the woods or walking along a lonesome road or at my home which is a farmhouse. The actual development of my ideas is done by others under my constant supervision. Long experience has taught me not to expect prompt results. Many failures invariably precede success. Some of my inventions have come after years of thought and effort. Occasionally, however, the results are reasonably prompt." (H. E. Warren)

"There is usually no initial procedure in a real invention. The idea simply comes to one in the process of his work. The real procedure begins after the inception of the initial idea, and this is very important. You consider first the idea with respect to its economic value. Second, whether it is mechanically practicable and whether it can be produced at a cost commensurate with its economic value. If the answer to any of these questions is 'No,' you stop right there if you are wise. If the answer is 'Possible—but not certain,' you give it continued thought and perhaps decide on some development that will give you more certain knowledge of its possibilities. If, in your opinion, the answer is positively 'Yes' to each of these propositions you naturally become intensely interested in the development. Third, having decided to go ahead, a very careful analysis is made of the possible methods to accomplish the end and of the mechanical details to be employed in working out the necessary construction. This is largely an application of judgment or experience to the problem in hand. It is purely a design proposition although subsidiary inventions often come about in this process. The analysis should be very searching, and it is even more important to reject unsound ideas than it is to perceive good ones. So far, the invention is entirely in your mind, or on paper, and has been studied quantitatively as well as qualitatively. This is important. Fourth, the next thing is to build the structure and find its defects (and possibly its advantages) which your mind did not perceive. If your initial work is very thorough and your experience in the field has been considerable, your first try-out may be quite successful. The principal further developments will come in time with use, rather than following immediately upon your experimental development. It is my contention from experience that development can be accomplished in mind and on paper at a great saving in both time and money." (W. H. Carrier)

"I first investigate all similar devices and methods of using same, to ascertain what has been done along the line I intend to follow. If the inventor can think up a new and better method of doing a certain piece of work the chances are there will be an opening for a new device. But to think up a new and better method is where the rub comes in. This requires constant thought until a conclusion is reached. But refusing to give up, an idea comes sooner or later. The next step is to work out a device. It is not difficult for one who is mechanically inclined. I generally start by making pencil sketches, checking good and bad points, following with a scale drawing from which I make a model, being ready then to make a test, although I never make a model until I feel quite sure I have something worth while, efficient, simple, of low manufacturing cost and having a good market value." (G. B. Bosco)

"An invention begins with the interesting things around you which seem to be in need of improvement. Then comes a study of the whole problem, as to the wisdom of such an improvement. It must be considered from the standpoint of the service it will render to the manufacturer or public, and the cost of such an improvement must be balanced with the service it will render. If this improvement will result in the saving of time, money or labor, or finds a new use for material, or results in an entirely new device which will find a ready market, then it becomes the inventor's problem. Quite often a problem is brought up by a request or public demand.

"The actual inventing becomes more or less a problem in mental mathematics—the addition and subtraction of materials; energy; motion—if the invention requires motive power, then the most economic power suitable to the application and location of a device should be used. If a peculiar movement is required all of the known movements are brought to the mental picture and, one by one, are added or subtracted, which may result in a combination of old ideas and new; one which may result in an entirely new device. The materials are next in line for study as to what the device should be made of, and a careful study into the nature of these materials and how they perform under the conditions to which they are to be subjected if the invention must be made.

"Up to this time, it is purely a mental picture which may involve hours, days or years to complete, and it may never be completed due to the fact, after the picture develops, that you begin to see the shortcomings in the invention—or it may develop into a thing of beauty that you can see will have an appeal and will actually be of great service. This 'mental painting'—as I call it—does not have to be continued until the job is finished. It can be taken up as you have time and worked on until it develops into a complete picture. As you take up the painting of this picture, you naturally go over it from the beginning and survey it, and if you are satisfied with what you have done on it so far, you go on building until it is complete.

"When this mental painting is complete, you then begin putting your idea into practice, either by the construction of a model or a drawing or a real picture. No artist has ever painted a material picture unless it might have been a copy, without having first painted a mental picture of his idea. I do not believe that any inventor has ever made an invention worth while without having unconsciously or consciously painted a mental picture of his idea; in the first place—he may have done some certain amount of experimental work along with the painting. This experimental work was only a process of 'paint mixing'—trying to obtain a 'right color' for his 'mental painting.' During this experimental or 'paint mixing' process, he may have developed a new 'color' or idea which is an inspiration for his next work." (F. F. Forshee)

"Inquiries are constantly being received by our companies from business houses as to whether the manufactured articles can be fitted into the particular needs of their business. I usually take the subject in hand and give my theories for experimentation and development to the technical or production department, as the case may be, and out of this naturally follows a series of conferences as models and samples are made. This invariably leads to other development work, which often carries with it a patentable idea and may lead to a major invention.

"At this point may I say that the problems usually come from outside through complaints and enlarged possibilities for the use of the product. And again, some competitor may have stolen a march in some direction, which necessitates intensive research and inventive activities on the part of our company." (G. R. Raymond)

"The first step in inventing is the recognition of the need for doing something in an entirely new way or improving an old method. This need manifests itself in one or more or all of the following forms. (a) The results being obtained with existing apparatus are not satisfactory for one or more reasons. (b) Existing apparatus becomes more or less obsolete by improved apparatus appearing in the field, making it necessary to improve old or develop new apparatus to meet competition. (c) The necessity of reducing production costs of existing apparatus. (d) Recognizing the potential demand for something entirely new or novel along any particular line.

"In general, the detailed steps followed in inventing are comparatively simple. The first step is making the decision that a certain invention is either necessary or desirable. The next step is to obtain a thorough understanding of why the invention is desirable or necessary. The next step is to fix the basic principles by which it must be worked out. The next step is to eliminate all past and present practices from the problem in order not to be hampered by tradition, convention or prejudice. The next step is to determine by selection and elimination which elements will be used and proceed to assemble them into the working structure which becomes the invention. The next step is to assume that errors will develop when working out the details (perhaps many of them) which will prevent the results ultimately hoped for from being obtained and be prepared to patiently set out to correct them." (R. A. Foresman)

"My procedure in inventing varies with circumstances, but I have relied very largely upon my own past experiences. I have subscribed for many years to leading technical publications and I have followed carefully the proceedings of technical societies. In most cases I have had ample facilities in my own factory or laboratory to arrange rough set-ups to demonstrate fundamentals before going into any refinements. Where results seemed promising I have checked up on theories, and finally I have made thorough Patent Office searches. Most of my successes have come about through more or less complete failure of the things I have started out to do and bitter disappointment has seemed to stimulate me to greater effort, bringing success in unexpected directions." (Samuel W. Rushmore)

CHAPTER VI

THE MENTAL PROCESSES OF THE INVENTOR

IN THE preceding chapter a general description of the inventor at work was given. We shall now attempt to see what mental processes are going on when he is inventing. The inventor's mind resembles a psychic crucible or an alembic in which he mixes or distills his experiences out of which are formed new inventions. What is the nature of this process? What does actually happen? What conditions favor this process?

We have already seen that invention in its broadest aspect is a fundamental human activity. We begin to invent from the moment we are born. Every act of adaptation to our environment amounts to invention. All learning processes are fundamentally inventive in nature. Invention ultimately resolves itself into an intelligent adaptive act of behavior adequate to a given situation or need. The mental processes of invention, therefore, go deeply into the roots of the basic problems of human psychology.

It has been previously stated that the first essential event in the process of invention is the recognition or experience of a need and the effort to satisfy it. The need may have its origin in the basic human wants such as hunger and sex or it may be a need imposed from without by economic and social conditions. These needs act as powerful drives, incentives or stimuli to action. The important thing in the situation which leads to inventive effort is an obstacle which prevents the satisfaction of the need by a direct response. The thwarting of this direct response leads to an emotional reaction with further efforts for the satisfaction of the need. These efforts take on a trial and error aspect because the direct means of satisfaction are not available and no other means are yet known. The first attempts to satisfy any need are those which are most direct and best known. When these fail the efforts become more and more indirect by the process of trial and error. The efficacy of the indirect method is described by such terms as ingenuity, sagacity, insight or intelligence.

This situation is well illustrated by the following experiment. Let us put a dog in a cage provided with a trip escape-latch which will permit his release, if properly manipulated. Now let us starve this dog for a few days and put a tempting piece of red meat just outside the cage in his full view. He immediately dashes at the meat but fails to reach it because he is restrained by the bars. A profound emotional response ensues followed by violent efforts such as clawing, poking, biting, scratching, and pushing. The dog will naturally make many useless and random movements until by chance he touches the trip lever which releases him, thereby giving him access to the meat.

Now let us put a man in a similar cage under the same conditions. When food is placed near the cage he may go through the same behavior shown by the dog but he may instead stand perfectly still in the center of the cage. Visibly he is doing nothing, but mentally he is going through all the behavior shown by the dog. Instead of actually manipulating the objects around him he manipulates the symbols of these objects mentally. The trip latch may finally attract his attention and upon manipulation he is released.

Inventive behavior, although usually not so simple as in this experiment, involves exactly the same kind of reactions. The inventor experiences a need which he wishes to satisfy. Direct efforts fail. An emotional response is naturally caused by this frustration of effort. Further efforts both mental and physical ensue until he finds a way to satisfy his want. Now the interesting aspect of this inventive process is that most of the efforts are first made mentally. The inventor manipulates the symbols of his past experience mentally and only after a satisfactory solution is obtained by a mental trial and error behavior does he actually attempt to satisfy the need.

The following highly interesting story of a prisoner who made some very ingenious inventions will illustrate very graphically the mental processes in making an invention: "A few years ago in one of our western State penitentiaries a convict escaped by the old manner of cutting through his bars. He was at liberty only a few weeks or months when the police picked him up and returned him to his shadowed house. The prison officials, as is common in such cases, demanded to know where the man got his saw. He shook his head with dejected doggedness and said he'd used none. Guffaws among the wardens. Still the man blinked, held himself in a kind of stupor and insisted that he had not used a saw, that no one had smuggled such an instrument to him and that he had been without accomplices. The keepers menaced him and applied their tongue starters. Their victim bore the pain as best a man can in silence. They tossed him into the dungeon where he lay groaning but spoke no word.

"Eventually, the many won another of those struggles which the ego seems destined to lose. The escaper gave sign that he was willing to talk. They dragged him from his hole and he shuffled away to the machine shop, where he looked about and finally picked up a bit of twine. This he dipped into the glue-pot at the far end of the building, where the carpentry was done. He carried it dripping back to a steel table where some emery was lying about and twisted his sticky string in the powder. As it dried the bits of emery held fast and he had a moderately effective contrivance for an immoderately patient and determined man. He said it had taken him three months to cut through the bars in this fashion. The officials believed him and so set down the case upon their books.

"They put this remarkable escaper into another cell and took precautions against the abstraction of twine and glue and emery powder. Nevertheless, at the end of about three and a half years, the same man again made his escape and his bars showed that they had been cut through in exactly the same manner as before.

"The prison intelligences began to waken at this. The man had not had access to glue or emery or twine this time. As a matter of fact, he had before the previous escape been employed in a quarter of the prison which must have made it impossible for him to visit the shops and get string after string of glue emery. The convict had hoaxed them.

"This time they did not get the bar cutter back, but his story is well known among the underworld élite. The man had used nothing but woolen strings carefully drawn from the rough stockings furnished by the State. These he had moistened in his own spittle and then rolled in the dust of his floor, sticking them against the stones of his cell wall till they had partly dried. With these frail strands he had attacked the inch-thick steel bars.

"At night, when he had been locked in his cell and the lights-out signal given, this giant of patience had crept from his couch and begun pulling his sandy string back and forth across a bar. It took many nights before he made an impression, taking a few swipes at the bar, then listening intently for the rubber shod footfall of the roundsman, then swiping again at the cage, till the night was half spent. He got little sleep. They worked him hard in the brickyard. He lost weight and grew ill. Still he did not give up. He suspended his work for a time, till strength returned. At last he had one of the two necessary bars cut almost through, so that a quick wrench would jerk it from its place. He smeared the cut with earth and lime and touches of green paint and red brick dust, and so he attacked the second. The prison officials did not suspect him. They made cursory examinations of his cell but did not sound the bars. Besides this man was an emery user and he had none.

"Slowly again then, like the drop of water on the slab of granite, like frost and thaw at the heart of a crag, like time itself against the mountains of the world, this insuperable man went on to cut the single bar that stood against his freedom—a thing most likely empty, a mere word. It took him almost all of three and one-half years to do this deed of forfeit valor and sublime tenacity. Once ready, he rested and ate his fill again, so that his strength might not fail him, once his foot was on open ground. Then one night when the moon was beyond the world rim and clouds had soiled the faces of the Pleiades, he was gone." [1]

Now let us analyze the mental processes of this prisoner. We first have a clearly defined and powerful desire of escape. This desire is very complex consisting of many other unsatisfied desires implicated in the denial of his personal liberty and all the normal activity that goes with it. The first response would probably be simple and direct. It would be an attempt to break the bars or to pull them apart, but he cannot do this with his hands. Our prisoner's memory now begins to work. Past experiences began to be recalled vividly. Ways of escape suggest themselves—kill the guard, jump over the wall, pick the lock, but in mental analysis they do not seem feasible. If he only had a saw he could cut the bars, but no saw is available. Finally the thread and emery are combined in an astonishing manner. How did this happen? Most of us would say imagination. We could also say he reasoned it out knowing the physical properties of the materials available to him. What really happened was a chance combination of the mental elements of his past experiences forming a new pattern or a new relationship of known things. We know from actual anatomical study of the brain that there are millions of

[1] E. H. Smith, The criminal as an inventor, Scientific American, 1924, 130, 376-7, 426.

neurones which are the basis of mental activity and that the brain structure is so constituted that an infinite number of neural connections are possible. The thwarting of the normal satisfaction of our prisoner's desires caused a powerful emotional reaction with a tendency to overt and direct action. But this direct action being impossible in his situation, a great deal of mental activity will naturally ensue. Many past experiences and memories arise due to the activation of the entire neural structure of the brain.

A great many neural connections were thus made in his brain in this emotional condition. Many neural patterns were made from the elements of his past experiences until the combination, string, glue and emery were formed and consciously perceived. Mental manipulation of this pattern with actual conditions indicated that it was feasible. It was then actually tried out and it proved to be effective, as we have seen. We can readily conceive that many other patterns formed under this emotional tension were perceived by the prisoner. Each one was then manipulated and tried out mentally by the tests of past experience. Many patterns were probably so weak in configuration and loosely organized that our prisoner was not aware of them. The entire situation surrounding the prisoner was one which constantly aroused an emotional reaction and the desire to escape. This state of affairs might go on for days, months and years. Suddenly there is a flash of insight, a wonderful exuberance of feeling, tensioning of the muscles, the emotion of joy, a great psychic relief and a renewed flow of energy. What happened? This endless play of neural connections caused by his emotional condition induced by his situation finally gave a successful pattern. Mental trial shows it to be entirely practicable and possible. The great emotional tension of our prisoner finds its release into activity which coupled with a new emotional response produced by the knowledge of freedom within reach gives an astonishing supply of renewed effort and energy for the final act.

We thus see that the essential psychological feature of invention is a mental trial and error process produced under emotional conditions caused by an unsatisfied desire or need resulting in an adequate act of behavior which satisfies the need. Of course, not all inventions are made under the extreme emotional conditions of the prisoner, but unquestionably in all creative effort there is a decided emotional tone. Every need which cannot be satisfied at once, every problem which cannot be readily solved, causes a distinct emotional tension, restlessness and discomfort which is followed by active exertion and effort, physical as well as mental. Under these conditions a great deal of neural activity takes place in the brain with the consequent formation of many patterns from the elements of past experience which have already left their effects in the brain structure. The formation of these patterns appears to be largely dependent upon the particular individual involved, the degree of emotional reaction and his past experience.

It is interesting to note that many inventors attribute the formation of the mental patterns to the subconscious mind. The sudden flashes and inspirations which they experience have led many of them to believe that some mental process has been going on which has solved the problem for them while they were engaged in other activities or even when asleep. The assumption that the subconscious is responsible for the final solution is, however, no answer to the problem. It merely amounts to giving a name to a thing which puzzles and mystifies us. The formation of neural patterns depends upon many physiological and chemical conditions in the body. The inventor may attack a problem for months or years without attaining a solution. But some day the proper conditions prevail which are favorable for the formation of a sought-for pattern and it is in these moments that the so-called flashes and inspirations occur. In this connection it is interesting to quote the statement of Herrick as a neurologist: "That which is most characteristic of human cortical activity is just that flexibility or plasticity of organization which facilitates the formation of innumerable transient associational patterns which have no enduring quality. In advance of any overt act we 'think through' many provisional solutions of a problem of conduct, discarding one after another before the right course of overt action is found. . . . It is the capacity to do this sort of thing that most sharply differentiates men from rats. These powers of imagination, of 'free association,' of invention, of idealization, depend upon the fluidity of the intracortical organization and the preservation of its plasticity." [2]

Inventors and creative workers are thus largely differentiated from their fellow men by their emotional reaction to needs which they experience and the openness of neural connection in their brains. It has often been said that necessity is the mother of invention. In one sense this is true because necessity is the need which initiates the inventive process. We must remember, however, that besides the necessity we must have an individual who reacts with the proper emotional intensity to the need so as to produce an invention. The necessity, however, must not be too great or extreme as it would be in a situation involving fear or danger with the consequent instinctive and uncontrolled behavior. There has been a necessity for many inventions long before they were produced. Take the sewing-machine, for instance. All the mechanical elements necessary to make the sewing-machine were known long before it was invented. No one will deny that a sewing-machine was a great necessity long before it was invented. Yet why was it not invented? The reason is that this necessity was not recognized or felt as a need by an individual who had a sufficient emotional reaction to the problem to initiate the inven-

[2] C. J. Herrick, Brains of rats and men, Chicago, Univ. of Chicago Press, 1926, 349-350.

tive process and who in addition had the requisite past experience giving him the mental elements out of which a satisfactory pattern could be made. No doubt the necessity of the sewing-machine had aroused an emotional reaction in many people but either the intensity of the emotional reaction was insufficient or if it was sufficient it did not occur in an individual who had the proper experience with which to make the new patterns to satisfy the need.

On the other hand, when several individuals having the proper emotional reaction and the requisite past experience are confronted with the same need, we are bound to have simultaneous and multiple inventions. This actually occurs quite often. The Patent Office records show that hundreds of identical inventions are made each year by individuals living in widely scattered parts of the country and entirely out of contact with each other. The question of multiple invention is highly interesting and will be discussed fully in Chapter VIII.

The conditions initiating invention have been designated as a creative drive by Woodworth, the drive being a chain of reaction systems having temporary control of the inventor and directing his activity toward his goal. In his "Dynamic Psychology" he states that "the tendency that furnishes the drive for originative behavior—which, as already suggested, emphatically needs a drive, since it runs counter to the ease of routine—must, according to some authors, be furnished by some one of the great primal instincts common to man and animals. Danger, hunger as the type of economic need, rivalry, and sex impulse, have most often been assigned as the motive force, and any of them may certainly furnish the drive. But there is no reason for thus limiting the possibilities. The motive force may be one of those added to the native stock in the experience of the individual; and, as the genius has shown us, it may be an objective interest. It is impossible to believe that Gauss, so absorbed in his mathematical discoveries as to be oblivious to hunger and the appeals of his friends, is driven by hunger, rivalry, or sex impulse, or in fact, by anything but his interest in what he is doing; and the same is true in a humbler way of the devoted labors of lesser men. This point has already been sufficiently insisted upon. The drive may be any tendency to action which, once aroused and not immediately satisfied, continues awake and so in a position to supply impetus to other mechanisms. Any drive, obstructed, may give rise to originative activity.

"The conditions that excite original activity are, then, an awakened tendency toward some result and an obstruction encountered. If we would know the form of activity by which the obstruction is overcome, and the factor of originality revealed in action, we shall have to examine such comparatively humble instances as can be brought under experimental control, hoping that our results here will be applicable also to the higher manifestations of originality; for it is quite possible that the form of the process is the same in humble and noble instances, the difference lying in the field of exercise rather than in the form of the activity." [3]

"In general, then, the process gone through in original activity has the form of varied reaction and trial and error, with some degree of control and generalization. The process may be restated thus: the individual is confronted by a situation to which he attempts to react but meets with obstruction. This stimulates him to exploration and varied attempts at escape. The situation, being complex, offers many points of attack, many features which, being observed, suggest or evoke reactions in accordance with past experience. The difficulty is to find the right feature to react to, or, in other words, so to perceive the situation as to be able to bring our existing equipment into successful use. The individual whose past experience has equipped him for reaction to this type of situation, who has most flexibility combined with

[3] R. S. Woodworth, Dynamic psychology, New York, Columbia Univ. Press, 1918, 138-139.

due persistence and control, and who is natively most responsive to this type of situation, displays the most originality in dealing with it." [4]

The inventor is thus characterized by an innovating attitude toward his environment. He has a permanent set or adjustment which is put into action by an obstacle, difficulty or need. He is characterized by an emotional response to any situation requiring the inventive process for its solution. The innovating activity very often becomes an end in itself on account of the extreme satisfaction experienced thereby. We all know the great joy experienced in creation, the feeling of superiority and exhilaration. The inventor, therefore, may seek to find new needs and to meet them in order to experience the thrill of creation again and incidentally to satisfy many other motives of which he may not be aware consciously.

Invention has been until now explained by saying that it is due to the "inventive faculty" or the "imagination." The courts are especially fond of using such expressions as "the inventive faculty" or "the inventive genius." The term inventive faculty implies that the inventor possesses a distinct faculty not found in other people. This view is entirely untenable in the light of modern psychology. Mental faculties do not exist in our brain, as such, each performing its own function. On the contrary we react to stimuli as a whole, not only with our bodies but also with our brains. Any specific mental activity cannot be confined to a single faculty. On the contrary, the entire nervous system of the organism is involved.

Imagination has been discussed a great deal in the older books on psychology as a mental faculty. This term, however, is useful to designate a certain type of mental activity. We say a man has a good imagination, an artist has a creative imagination. We mean by this that they are able to recombine their past experience into

[4] R. S. Woodworth, Dynamic psychology, New York, Columbia Univ. Press, 1918, 144.

new and original patterns. Several kinds of imaginations have been distinguished, such as reproductive, constructive, and creative. The reproductive imagination refers to the simple recall of past experiences. In this sense it is practically the same as memory. Constructive imagination reproduces the constructive arrangements of experience and creative imagination forms arrangements which did not have a previous existence. According to Hollingworth: "Imagination is invention and invention consists in the arrangement of old materials in new modes of organization." [5]

The materials out of which the mental process of imagination builds its patterns are past experiences. Imagination may produce patterns which never existed before but the elements of the patterns are old and can be found in the past experience of the individual. The irresistible human tendency of manipulation and exploration of objects found in our environment begins at an early age. It is probably the basis of curiosity and playfulness. Manipulation supplies much of the necessary experience for our imagination. According to Watson [6] it is one of the original tendencies of human beings upon which are built all later habit formations. Inventiveness and constructiveness are thus to a large extent dependent on our manipulative tendencies. Manipulation first begins with the random movements of an infant. These movements are probably due to the metabolic processes of the infant's physiological activity. As the random movements become more coordinated manipulation and exploration begin.

Woodworth says that "the human enterprise of exploration runs the gamut from simple exploratory movements of the sense organs in looking and listening, to the elaborate scientific procedure followed in testing

[5] H. L. Hollingworth, Psychology, its facts and principles, New York, Appleton, 1928, 281.

[6] J. B. Watson, Psychology from the standpoint of a behaviorist, Phila., Lippincott, 1919, 260.

hypotheses and discovering the laws of nature. Inventive or manipulative activity runs a similar gamut from the child's play with his toys to the creation of a work of art, the designing of a work of engineering, the invention of a new machine, or the organization of a new government. The distinction between the two lines of activity is that exploration seeks what is there, and manipulation changes it to something else. Exploration seeks the facts as they exist, while invention modifies or rearranges the facts. The two enterprises go hand in hand, however, since facts must be known to be manipulated, while on the other hand manipulation of an object brings to light facts about it that could never be discovered by simple examination.

"Beginning with grasping, turning, pushing, pulling, shaking and dropping of objects, the child's manipulation develops in several directions. One line of development leads to manual skill. The child learns to manage his toys better.

"A second line of development is in the direction of constructiveness. Taking things apart and putting them together, building blocks, assembling dolls and toy animals into 'families' or 'parties,' setting table or arranging toy chairs in a room, are examples of this style of manipulation, which calls less for manual dexterity than for seeing ways in which objects can be rearranged.

"Make-believe is a third direction followed in the development of manipulation. The little boy puts together a row of blocks and pushes it along the floor, asserting that it is a train of cars. The little girl lays her doll carefully in its bed, saying 'My baby's sick; that big dog did bite him.' This might be spoken as 'manipulating things according to the meanings attached to them' the blocks being treated as cars, and the doll as a sick baby.

"Perhaps a little later than make-believe to make its appearance in the child is story-telling, the fourth type of manipulation. Where in make-believe he has an actual object to manipulate according to the meaning attached to it, in story-telling he simply talks about persons and things and makes them perform in his story." [7]

Manipulation thus finally gives us symbols for our experiences which we can manipulate mentally and form into new patterns. It is interesting to remember that play often consists of random manipulation and experimentation. This is a deep-seated tendency in all human beings manifesting itself from infancy to senility. Many inventors regard their inventive activity as a form of play and they enjoy it for the manipulative pleasure they obtain from it.

In addition to manipulation which we have discussed as supplying materials for the imagination we must not overlook simple observation which is probably an outgrowth of manipulation. Simple observation leads to perception which is really an elementary mental pattern. When we perceive something we immediately begin to compare our perception with similar experiences which we might have had in the past. We probably perceive things and recognize them as having been in our past experience because they arouse a similar neural activity in our brain. Mental life thus appears to be based largely on mental patterns, and as we have seen, invention is also entirely based on the formation of complex patterns from simpler patterns. Aristotle in his "Art of Poetry" has described genius as the power or faculty of seeing resemblances amid a multitude of differences. This is also true of the inventor who can see analogies, relations and similarities where others can only see isolated facts and unrelated objects. The inventor has the ability to form new patterns by virtue of the same activity with which he makes his perceptions. The ability to see resemblances amid a multitude of differences is really the result of the mental manipulation of newly formed patterns by a trial and error process in order to test them out by former experiences.

---

[7] R. S. Woodworth, Psychology, New York, Holt, 1921, 481-482.

In this connection we might quote from Varendonck: "I conclude by saying that synthesis, in establishing analogies between objects which were previously dissimilar is not only invention itself, it is also the genesis of perception and therefore of conception, for it is the necessary and sufficient condition for it. With no remembrance of the relations of similitude the phenomenon of perception could not occur any more than that of conception. The anterior developments will have sufficed to establish this. On the other side, the same form of synthesis, namely, in invention, operates with elements resulting from perception and conception, so that the conclusion follows that no one of these three psychic operations can dispense with the others. They jointly constitute the essential mechanisms of intelligence." [8]

We have seen from our analysis of the inventive process that the term imagination refers to the mental activity which produces the new patterns from past experience while the inventor is under the drive to satisfy his need. It has been generally recognized that imagination is the basis of invention. We have seen that the inventors themselves and all those who are in close touch with them believe that imagination is an essential requisite in inventing. This is entirely correct. However, the emotional background of this process has until now been entirely overlooked which is highly important, as we have seen. The statement that invention is imagination is thus not an explanation or a definition for it is only part of the story.

It has been customary to draw a sharp line between imagination and reasoning or thinking. Our actual mental processes, however, do not submit to such an arbitrary classification. Mental life consists of the constant energizing and stimulation of the neurones of our nervous system, particularly of the brain. Day-dreaming is a good example of the activity when it is not directed to-

[8] J. Varendonck, The evolution of the conscious faculties, London, Allen and Unwin, 1923, 154.

ward an immediate end. Day-dreaming is thus a form of unrestrained imagination by which many loose patterns are formed from past experiences. When this process, however, becomes more controlled and the patterns which are formed are tested by reality and actual past experiences we have a mental process which is termed reasoning or thinking. Imagination and reasoning are thus essentially the same. Imagination is the formation of mental patterns and reasoning is a mental trial and error testing these patterns by previous experience. Our analysis of the inventive process thus shows that not only imagination but also reasoning is involved in the making of every invention.

According to Woodworth reasoning is mental exploration as distinguished from purely motor exploration of the trial and error variety. "When you have described reasoning as a process of mental exploration, you have told only half the story. The successful reasoner not only seeks, but finds. He not only ransacks his memory for data bearing on his problem, but he finally 'sees' the solution clearly. The whole exploratory process culminates in a perceptive reaction. What he 'sees' is not presented to his senses at the moment, but he 'sees' that something must be so. This kind of perception may be called inference.[9]

"Imagination thus presents a close parallel to reasoning, where also, there are two stages, the preliminary consisting in getting the premises together and the final consisting in perceiving the conclusion. The final response in imagination is in general like that in reasoning; both are perceptive reactions; but imagination is freer and more variable. Reasoning is governed by a very precise aim, to see the actual meaning of the combined premises; that is it is exploratory; while imagination, though it is usually more or less steered either by a definite aim or by some bias in the direction of agreeable results, has

[9] R. S. Woodworth, Psychology, New York, Holt, 1921, 465.

after all much more latitude. It is seeking, not a relationship that is there, but one that can be put there." [10]

Memory is another of the faculty terms used a great deal by the older psychologists to designate the ability to recall past experience. Memory actually includes not only the recall of mental experience but also the repetition of learned behavior. As we have seen, the inventive process relies mainly on past experience for the material out of which it forms the new patterns. Memory is, therefore, highly important for invention. Under the drive of a need past experiences are revived and formed into new combinations.

It is well known that many creative workers such as musicians, artists, and inventors are highly temperamental. This trait has puzzled most psychologists but we can readily see the reason for it from our analysis of the inventive process. Creative workers show an unusual emotional reaction to obstacles which they meet, and we should, therefore, expect to find similar reactions in other situations in life. In many instances this is actually the case, resulting in the so-called temperamental personality. Slight, ordinary obstacles do not arouse in the average person very much of an emotional response, at least, not sufficient to be noticeable; however, in creative workers these obstacles arouse an unusual reaction on account of their emotional makeup. Creative workers seem to have a great nervous sensibility. Their powers of observation are very keen and they react to all stimuli with more than a normal amount of response. They seem to have excess energy which is liberated on the slightest provocation.

Henry A. Wise Wood, the well-known inventor of the autoplate machine, states in this connection the following:

"One of my characteristics from birth has been an intolerance of any obstacle that stood in the way of whatever I wished to accomplish. Were such an obstacle

---

[10] R. S. Woodworth, Psychology, New York, Holt, 1921, 520.

thought beyond one's powers to remove it the fact constituted a challenge and made me throw myself with all my mind into the work of getting it out of my way—this of course if the obstacle were worth removing."

We have seen that external obstacles in our environment initiate the process of invention. On the other hand, existing internal obstacles do not have the same effect. Our mental processes follow the universal law of the path of least resistance. Mental activity produced by an emotional response to an obstacle will naturally follow the old and acquired paths of neural activity already existing because they are the paths of least resistance. It is for this reason that so few human individuals are original or inventive. We are by nature conservative and bound by our learned habits.

As Usher says in his "History of Mechanical Inventions": "New syntheses are made difficult because we have become accustomed to ignore certain types of perceptions or images. In many respects, our conscious faculties are biased in favor of conservatism. Our reasoning powers are primarily occupied with the organization of past experience. Our will is chiefly concerned with the maintenance of the honor of the personality that has already been created. The bias of reason is perhaps the more important in connection with the problems of invention. After all, it is a wholly natural circumstance, for reason works mainly by analysis towards critical ends. The inventor, however, by his unusual and excessive reaction to a need liberates so much energy that he overcomes this internal resistance and overflows figuratively his usual neural paths into new paths thus forming new patterns." [11]

According to Varendonck "the comparative slowness with which originality is reached is explained by the fact that it has no existing psychic path at its disposal. The two streams which flow together must not only seek to

[11] A. P. Usher, A history of mechanical inventions, New York, McGraw-Hill, 1929, 28.

meet by leaving their old beds, but their confluence must satisfy certain conditions established beforehand and dictated by the principle of similitude." [12]

There is apparently a great inertia or resistance in the average person to initiate the innovating process. When we imitate we are merely following learned behavior or our habits. This has been well expressed by Woodworth as follows: "The ordinary man, followed through his day's routine reveals little originality. Surrounded for the most part by familiar objects, he perceives them in the old ways or neglects them as he is wont. He meets the regular demands made on him by the regular acts that he has learned to make. Even if the objects that confront him are somewhat novel, he assimilates them to familiar types of objects, and makes little response to their novelty; and even if the conditions he has to meet are somewhat new, he comes through as best he may, with his old stock of reactions. The inertia of habit carries him along; and as he has become pretty well adapted to his circumstances, habit carries him along pretty smoothly. Yet some embers of originality are still smouldering within him and can be fanned into life when conditions are right." [13]

We have already noted the similarity in the mental processes involved in learning and invention. It is well known that old persons seldom learn new habits. They usually meet their problems by their old and familiar ways. The age distribution of inventors shows that there are very few active inventors of advanced age. The most productive period is from 20 to 50. Very few inventions are made by men under eighteen because they have not had the necessary experience and probably have had no incentives to invent.

Knowlson states "that the real commencement of the productive mental life synchronizes with puberty; it is

---

[12] J. Varendonck, The evolution of the conscious faculties, London, Allen and Unwin, 1923, 146.

[13] R. S. Woodworth, Dynamic Psychology, New York, Columbia Univ. Press, 1918, 136-137.

the time when imagination and emotion assert themselves and seek new objects and new forms." He also states "that in old age the loss of generative power is accompanied by the loss of mentally creative power." [14] This agrees with Ribot in his "Creative Imagination."

An interesting feature of the inventive process is that it cannot be controlled. The formation of new mental patterns seems to be a matter of so-called inspiration, flash or happy thought. When a problem is presented and all the necessary data for its solution are marshalled, a period of incubation appears to be usually necessary. This may take days or years. There may be intense mental concentration and searching. Many inventors relate that they get their ideas when they least expect them. As was already stated after a need is experienced for which no solution can be found a great mental activity is initiated. A great many loose mental patterns are formed, many of which may not be perceived. Very often when engaged in an entirely different problem or activity the solution will flash. This is most likely due to the chance formation of a new pattern of which the inventor becomes conscious. The time element appears to be a highly important factor because the inventor must allow many neural patterns to form. Good physical condition, rest, and general emotional conditions may favor the openness of the neural connections so that the successful pattern is formed. The inventor must undergo a period of "masterful idleness" so to speak. A new fact found or an accidental observation made during this period may furnish the clue to the sought-for solution. The missing element of the pattern is thus often found by chance but being perceived its significance is at once grasped by the inventor who proceeds immediately to complete his unfinished pattern.

In order to induce a favorable condition to pattern formation inventors often resort to putting themselves in a creative mood by various expedients. Some will take long walks, others are stimulated by sketching on paper,

[14] T. S. Knowlson, Originality, New York, Lippincott, 1918, 138.

while some recline on a cot in a quiet room. Many of the idiosyncrasies of literary authors and artists are merely attempts to create this much sought-for creative mood or atmosphere.

Quoting from Knowlson's book on "Originality": "Ibsen used to keep a number of little images on his writing desk; they helped him in his work of composition, he said, but declined to say how, adding: 'That is my secret.' Similarly, Kant used a certain tower, visible from his study window, as a sort of mental focus for thinking out his categories; and when in the course of time, some trees grew up and hid the tower, he wrote to the City Council asking them to cut down the trees so that he might once more see the tower, and think. The story goes that the City Fathers complied. Buffon's eccentricities are well known, the chief among which was his inability to think to good purpose except in full-dress. Shelley found that munching bread was helpful in composing, just as Addison and Sheridan liked to have a bottle of wine handy, and Schiller a flask of Old Rhenish—also rotten apples in his desk. Gautier said: 'It is only the smell of printer's ink that can make me move.' Dr. Johnson needed a purring cat, and orange peel and tea within reach. Jokai could not write unless he had violet ink: black and blue ink would make work impossible; it had to be either violet ink or a lead pencil. Thomas Hardy, prior to beginning work, always removes his boots or slippers. (Most of these details are found in Erichsen's Methods of Authors.) Charles Lamb's sister says that Elia could do nothing in a room with bare and white-washed walls; that was the kind of room in which Stevenson could work to advantage. The contrasts in habit are as striking as it is possible to imagine; for whilst Rousseau liked to think out his pages bareheaded, in the sun, Bossuet preferred to work in a cold room, his head wrapped in furs; and Zola pulled down the blinds at mid-day because he found more stimulus in artificial light. Ribot remarked that 'some require motor excitation, they work only when walking or else prepare for work by physical exercise.' ('The Creative Imagination,' p. 73) And yet there are others who, like Milton, Descartes, Leibnitz, and Rossini, find the horizontal position more advantageous. ('The Influence of Bodily Posture on Mental Activities' by E. E. Jones)" [15]

WHAT INVENTORS HAVE TO SAY ABOUT INSPIRATIONS

The following remarks of inventors are quoted to show the very interesting and instructive manner in which they get their "hunches" or "inspirations" and under what circumstances they occur.

"A problem presents itself for which I cannot find an existing solution. I immediately eject it from the objective side of my mind, that is to say, I cease to labor over it, and consign it to the subjective 'department' of my mind. There it is taken in charge and one solution or another comes to the surface from time to time, that is, comes within sight of the objective side of my mind. If the solution is satisfactory I take hold of it and apply it; if it is not, I drop the problem again into my subjective mind and let it lie until it is ready to come out again. These emergences of solution occur at all sorts of times; usually early in the morning when I am just coming into consciousness. Then my mind seems to be clearest and my subconscious mind nearest the surface of objective thought. At other times solutions seem suddenly to present themselves, while I am reading, talking, at sea or even when busy with wholly different matters." (Henry A. Wise Wood)

"The first thing I do is to determine, as far as possible, all forms of construction on the market. If I feel an improvement can be made I give the subject a short concentrated thought and thus sort of hand it over to the back-

---

[15] T. S. Knowlson, Originality, New York, Lippincott, 1918, 107-108.

ground of my thought while active with my work as superintendent. Sometimes at lunch or before retiring I may make a few marks on the back of an envelope taken from my pocket. Sometimes a detail will appear to have worked itself out satisfactorily while I am watching a picture show. At the end of a week, or maybe a month, I have all important points completed (in my own mind, only). The whole thing is then turned over to one or more draftsmen to whom I give rough, free-hand sketches and sufficient verbal information to enable them to complete the job." (J. Manson)

"Ideas come when I least expect them, often when I am half asleep or day-dreaming. So far as I can remember I have had no good basic ideas when waiting for them. This has puzzled me considerably and as near as I can tell at present it seems to be an action of the subconscious mind when my conscious mind is dreaming or wandering. Great care must be taken to differentiate between the flash of a basic idea and subsequent design or development. I happen to be an engineer and furnish very largely basic ideas to either draftsmen or highly skilled mechanics for development. The invention proper is over with the conception of the basic idea." (R. N. Kircher)

"I have waked out of sound sleep with a new idea. Sometimes when I am dressing or shaving or tying a shoestring. Sometimes after hours or days of sweating over the drafting table. But most often when my mind is fresh and rested and free from worry or care and when I am approaching a new subject so that I am thinking in qualitative terms." (William Spruce Bowen)

"I usually keep the thought or idea in mind as much as possible. This does not mean that I think of the idea continually, but call it to mind as frequently as you would any subject you were very much interested in, and, as the details of the idea take form I make notes and sketches for reference. This may cover a period of from a few days to several years. Of course, if the time is long there may be periods of from several weeks to a couple of months time that the idea is not called to mind, but when it is I always notice some progress during the interim. As the idea becomes more complete a more concentrated effort and thought is put on it until the idea is completed.

"The following amplifies the foregoing procedure: I have put much thought on the subject of the evolution of new ideas, especially to that phase that apparently causes the individual to first create the complicated and then to simplify it. The simplified or completed idea is so obvious generally that it would appear to require more thought to create the complicated. In my own experience and observation the opposite is more generally true. The new ideas seem to occur about the same as the name of a street, town or person that you know as well as you know your own name, but cannot recall at the exact time you want it, but the fact that you want to remember the name started whatever action takes place in the mind which continued even though the initial thought was forgotten and perhaps five or ten minutes later the name comes clearly to your memory. So, too, the new idea you are seeking provided you have stored in your memory the various facts of knowledge necessary to produce the combination of thoughts that will create the new idea, if not, continued thinking will not bring results but if carried on over a sufficient period of time you may acquire the necessary additional knowledge which is necessary to combine with what you have to produce the new idea. I have experienced this on one or two occasions." (W. H. Wineman)

"My best inventions always come to me in a flash; by this I mean the fundamental idea. I may be at a concert, church, may be reading or talking when suddenly a new idea flashes through my mind. It is usually startling for it has no connection with what I am doing. Immediately the idea fills my mind forcing everything else out. I am usually amazed at the apparent simplicity of it. I reach for a piece of paper and with a few marks the general plan is before me, and my wife says that I say, 'By George that will certainly work.' Then I proceed to put it on the board and as I work it out ways develop, coming so fast that I wonder that the whole world hasn't done it before.

"Of course, you understand that I have been describing a new invention. When I am perfecting a machine the process is very different in the first stages. Then I study the need, and at some time the idea will come through in the way as above noted. It seems that I am simply a channel through which these inventions flow." (Howard Parker)

"When I attempt a new invention I buy a small blank book and carry it continuously. I make notes and sketches as fast as ideas come to mind—today I think I have the solution—I write it down and illustrate it. Tomorrow I find fault with it, find it won't work; this I jot down. Ideas come in periods of relaxation such as, riding home in a train. One of my happiest solutions came when I was listening to a sermon in church." (Spencer Miller)

"The problems presented themselves and in thinking over the best way to solve them, the ideas which were later patented, came to me. It may be of interest to know that in each case the basic idea came to me while I was in the bath-tub in the morning. My head is always clearer then and I am of course free from interruption." (D. H. Maury)

"I have had innumerable 'flash' ideas on the order of the invention of fiction. A few of these have developed some practical value. Many others have been abandoned because there did not appear to be a commercial demand to warrant further procedure. Frequently a search has disclosed anticipation by earlier inventors.

"With a few exceptions my inventions have been cold-blooded attempts to solve a problem presented in the course of my business. The first step is to give this problem and the proposed methods of meeting it, a ruthless 'third degree.' One of the worst dangers to an inventor is the tendency to 'kid himself,' that is to accept a solution which really does not fully satisfy him, but which he persuades himself is good enough. I have very frequently found, when confronted by anticipation after a patent search, that another and better way results from the necessity of giving the problem further study. Such of my schemes as have reached the market and met with any commercial success have gone through long periods of intensive design and development. I estimate that most successful inventions are the outcome of perhaps twenty per cent invention followed by eighty per cent engineering.

"An extended experience in examination of so-called inventions convinces me that the fearful mortality among these is due to failure to differentiate between real demands and imaginary ones. Much effort is wasted in the attempt to do something which does not need to be done. Utter lack of scientific training and knowledge of fundamental mechanical principles; laziness which deters the inventor from facing the heart-breaking grind which must follow conception in all but the simplest problems, are responsible for many failures." (John H. Barr)

"The need was apparent for something to accomplish a desired purpose and usually the other conditions of the problem would give some indication of how to start and by keeping at the problem a solution could usually be found. Some of the problems could not be solved this way and had to be laid aside. Often a solution would come to mind suddenly sometime afterward when engaged in other work. These cases seem to be the obvious results of subconscious thought.

"I have a very pronounced interest in schemes for electrical control of devices and can't help thinking about them, whether actually engaged in this work or not. It is only natural that ideas on how to do things either novel or improvements should come to mind." (W. S. H. Hamilton)

"I studied the problem, read all I could find pertaining to it, tested experimentally all the ideas that came to me, and sooner or later the right solution would flash on my mind often at the moment of awakening in the morning after a sound sleep." (T. A. Watson)

"An engineer may ask me in the course of a conversation, 'Can you make an instrument to measure and record the tearing strength of paper?' Quick as a flash all my past experience is at my command. I say 'Yes, there are at least two ways and I can do it.' I outline them roughly, thinking out loud as I use my pencil. Whether he promises to order one or not, I keep the problem in mind, thinking of it while lying awake between 2 and 3 or 4 A.M. and in the morning I wake with a distinct conviction that one of various schemes is the best. In my private room at the shop I make, with my own hands, a model changing various features as it grows till I am ready to turn it over to our superintendent who designs a commercial model. Only a fraction of the special instruments I invent and build, have a sufficient practical market to justify taking out patents. During the 18 years I was teaching physics I contrived many original devices some of which appear in the two textbooks I published." (Dr. Chas. B. Thwing)

"An idea may come to me from within, all of a sudden, like from the clear sky and at first all I may know is that I feel that certain results can be obtained without my knowing how to accomplish the desired results. Thinking about the problem for a while I turn to my everyday routine work trying to forget it. Then all of a sudden the problem bobs up in my mind. This may happen while I am busy with routine work, or reading the newspaper or a book at home, or on a train but more frequently at night in my sleep. I then stop my work or my reading if during the day, or wake up if it happens during my sleep, and mentally size up what subconsciously was prepared for me in the way of solving the problem. Invariably I find every time that the problem is nearer to solution. This encourages me to spend more and more of my conscious hours on thinking about the problem, but in most cases I find that the subconscious mind has done for me more than I could consciously accomplish thinking over the problem time and again. Waking up about 2 or 3 A.M. and lying in bed in perfect darkness I would suddenly have before me on the ceiling or on the wall every minute detail of a complicated wiring diagram of an automatic control system. Sometimes hundreds of wires would appear before me properly interconnected to accomplish just what I wanted to get in my conscious hours." (M. M. Goldenstein)

"I just construct equipment systems or apparatus as the case may be to attain desired results. At times ideas have bothered me for days and sometimes weeks until I set out to work them out to completion and then found that they amounted to invention. These are spontaneous ideas beyond control of the individual.

"I wish to dwell further on the latter part of my answer which I believe represents a certain quality or gift possessed by few. As stated previously I have found no rest for weeks at a time until I would finally seek seclusion and pencil in hand jot down certain things that would then reveal themselves but which previously were in unrecognizable form in my mind. Sometimes I did not know what they were about although I would be conscious of a constant urge in my mind to stop and interpret them into intelligent ideas. In most cases they were absolutely new ideas in the field to which they pertained. But I could not sit down and deliberately think out something that amounted to invention unless I knew of some necessary result to be attained. These forced inventions (forced on me whether I cared to bother with them or not) are to me very interesting for they appear to be due to a subconscious working of the mind, but in some cases they were entirely foreign to anything that I desired to perfect and often made me feel that perhaps they are God given from some unknown store of knowledge. Only after working out these thoughts to completion did I find mental rest and composure. They would occur sometimes at intervals of a few weeks to a number of months." (Thomas Appleby)

"Generally, I invent by first finding out a need or demand, and then casting about to see how it might be filled, efficiency and cost being considered. Frequently, ideas come like a bolt out of the blue, apparently suggested by something entirely different. The chain of suggestion skips rapidly from one idea to another, and is usually lost or forgotten, especially if it breaks loose while one is half asleep. On the original idea, many improvements and even substitutions are generally made." (Jerome Alexander)

"I first seek to analyze the fundamental conditions and requirements of the problem to be solved. I then find it necessary to overcome a natural feeling that probably the solutions which occur to me are old and do not merit further attention on my part. Having overcome this tendency, I then seek the most direct solution to the problem, endeavoring to apply at all times the simplest mechanical or chemical principles known to me. In this connection I make it a practice to keep in front of me the thought that there is no mechanical or chemical problem today which can not be solved in a commercial manner at some time and under some condition. This often guides me to a solution of the problem which I should have otherwise been afraid to undertake. I almost invariably make up my own drawings, at least of a preliminary nature and often I prepare the complete Patent Office drawings. One definite reason for this is the many times during the course of this work additional features or objects or results naturally present themselves to my mind as the invention evolves from stage to stage, and by doing my own work I can be in constant touch with these developments. This also makes it possible for me to endeavor to make each of them perform as many functions and purposes as possible. This result cannot always be accomplished but I should say that four times out of five the machine or device is greatly simplified by such an evolutionary process due to my own concentration on the problem in its details. This concentration is often extremely distasteful and requires time which is not always conveniently available, but in the long run it pays." (Thomas A. Banning, Jr.)

"I always aim for improvement by making machines, tools and equipment better, more efficient and if possible cheaper to manufacture. I never undertake to do anything in a field that I am not thoroughly familiar with. I study the problem for several days, sometimes weeks, without even putting a line on paper and finally I am able to make a mental picture of a machine or tool which I can see quite clearly with the principal parts functioning. The next step is that of making a complete drawing of same. Sometimes this process takes weeks and often when you think you have the proposition complete, you may see still a better way to accomplish the result. The final thing is to make actual models to try out and very often after this is done, further changes have to be made. I have always kept in mind, in trying to develop an invention, the commercial aspects of the proposition. In other words, would there be a demand for the particular machine or tool? Could it be made for less money than the cost of existing apparatus or machine in use? Would it accrue to the benefit of the particular industry within which it was to be used? Most of these questions would have to be answered in the affirmative in order to make it worth while, and if after the models are made the same function properly, an application for patent is the next step. My effort is usually applied on lines in which I am directly interested as a manufacturer. In other words, the patents I have obtained have nearly always been used in my own business and as a foundation to build on." (Frank Mossberg)

"After noting a deficiency, I set about to determine what it is, and what would be the most ideal capability of such an embodiment, without regard to the practicability of carrying it out. I then work to the end of approaching this ideal as closely as possible, while considering the practical and commercial aspects, having in mind that the feasible thing is not always practicable." (H. M. Friendly)

"The conception of the idea is a vague mental process, which may or may not be associated with some particular work. It is more generally associated with particular problems. The best ideas generally come after a good night's sleep and when the mind is not consciously occupied for the time being. The greatest difficulty occurs in bringing the idea into a clear and concise form so that it may be transferred to paper for record. The first records are generally very sketchy and sometimes inaccurate. In explaining the idea to others new features develop and finally a patent application is made out by an attorney which often does not clearly set forth the invention and must be revised and sometimes entirely rewritten to carry the true aspects of the invention.

"If inventions come naturally they come more patiently by constant practice. It has not been possible for me to make inventions on the spot when they were desired by others but it has been often possible to make desired inventions after an elapsed time from several days to several weeks or more.

"Inventions are most common when working alone and under quiet conditions, without too many facilities available. Often statements by others serve to make one conscious of ideas which would not otherwise be realized until a later date. These statements often are not connected with the idea at all but serve as a sort of a key." (Russell S. Ohl)

"The process of inventing begins with guessing, but a guess is not an invention. As soon as an inventor has made his first guess he subjects it to a sifting process in which the guess has to run the gauntlet of all the pertinent facts he can think of. The chances are a million to one that the first guess is discarded within the fraction of a second, and another takes its place. A thousand to one the second guess follows the first, but a little more slowly, and a third takes its place on the firing line. Usually this lasts a little longer, but it is a hundred to one that this also goes overboard and a fourth takes its place. A skilled inventor is liable to pass a hundred guesses in review in less time than it would take to explain one of them.

"A man's capacity as an inventor depends upon his faculty of making guesses which have some semblance of possibility to them, and the thoroughness with which he analyzes each guess to see if it is scientifically sound. An invention which is scientifically unsound, is a failure, and not an invention at all. It is a blunder, and a man cannot make many blunders and retain his standing as an inventor.

"Many inventors test each guess by physical experiment. I make most of my experiments with pencil and paper, or by sheer reasoning processes." (Casper L. Redfield) Some of these remarks were published in the *Westfield Medical Times*, June, 1929.

"I used to invent devices more or less for the joy of the thing. As a result of later commercial experience I now first consider the commercial possibilities of new devices or improvements in existing devices. I then recall all devices I have heard for accomplishing a similar result, and investigate their deficiencies and shortcomings. I then try to analyze the fundamental physical requirements to achieve the result desired, and try to keep these in mind during all of my subsequent thinking. This is desirable in order to avoid unnecessary complications in mechanism.

Preliminary thinking is done without the assistance of sketches although it may involve calculations to determine whether the fundamental concept is correct. After visualizing the device in my imagination I then make sketches in order to approach a practical structure. The next step is the making of models during which process the structure is usually further simplified to make it commercial for manufacture." (E. R. Stoekle)

"I have learned to concentrate my mind and thus develop a strong imagination, and in this way I can dream out mechanisms and other things and hold them in my mind and evolve them without making drawings to the point where when I do begin to draw them out the parts go together and function as previously imagined. Then I was already a draftsman—starting in as a boy at that work—so I had no difficulty in drawing out the ideas I had imagined or dreamed out." (William E. Williams)

"First there must be a demand for the solution of some problem. Every conceivable method then is called to mind that will contribute to this solution. The problem then is carried mentally for days. Now and then certain sketches will be made. After the mental image is formed and which has been reached by a process of elimination it is time to go into my private machine shop and laboratory and satisfy myself regarding certain principles and results. However, the idea is conceived in the mind. Any sketches made, tend to make more distinct the various ideas that come to one's mind." (A. L. Collins)

"Inventing seems to me to consist in the unconscious act of continual permutation of organized bits of knowledge I acquire by experiments and study. There seems also to exist in my mind some kind of a mechanism operating unconsciously to filter out of consideration those experiences and impressions which are not directly related with the particular problem my mind is occupied with. So, for instance, I cannot read systematically at these periods but usually glance through books and journals, noticing at once on the page just those words which directly concern the problem." (J. T. Tykociner)

"In contemplating a new invention, I always try first to outline in my mind as nearly as may be possible at that time what is the most desirable end to aim for. Next to the outline at least in my mind, if possible, three or four possible approaches to the solution of the problem. After that, if certain simple tests can be made to give any indication of the best choice, these should immediately follow. Oftentimes it will be found that the preliminary tests indicate something of real value and it has repeatedly happened in my experience that I felt the solution of the problem was close at hand. On further investigation, however, it usually appears that the simple tests, oftentimes first considered, do not cover the whole situation, and not infrequently I have discovered that the things which at first seemed to offer complete solution have little or nothing to do with the real practical solution; for example, in a spring suspension mechanism for automobiles on which I have spent some time; in the first instance, my conception of a solution of this problem was to design a spring which would absorb its own vibrations. This was simple in conception, and when I got the idea of how to do it, a very simple experiment indicated that it was easily possible to design such a spring. Knowing, however, the limitations of preliminary experiments, I decided to test more specifically under actual conditions to which the spring would be subjected in automobiles. To my astonishment, the spring which absorbed its own vibration seemed to be less satisfactory than the ordinary type of automobile spring. After some months of experimentation I finally reached the conclusion that it was the load which the spring carries and not so much the character of the spring, which controls in a spring suspension mechanism adapted to absorb all vibrations of the supported body in an automobile. I could cite other illustrations of a similar nature, but not so simple to illustrate.

I consider that no invention is completed until it has been tested thoroughly and under every conceivable condition in which it is likely to be placed in actual practice.

"To speak now more particularly from a standpoint of the psychology to be followed in inventing, I feel that first a particular perception of the conditions to be fulfilled must be attained then as particular and complete a perception of the possible ways of attacking a problem should be grasped. After meditation upon this including continual turning over in the mind of possible combinations and probable results with an intenseness of application which is seldom attained, in my case in any other activity, is the only way to really make an invention which will have actual value. In other words, it is a sort of super-logical deduction. By that I mean that the mere logical deduction from known values is not enough because the consciously known values are often not the only values which enter into the solution of the problem, and there is a kind of deduction which results from intense contemplation of cause and effect which in the last analysis outruns purely logical deduction from what could be consciously stated as known values. In other words, the mind seems to touch realities that we are not fully conscious of which may help to bring about the solution of a different problem, and when that solution is reached, it can then be stated in conscious terms and can easily be traced back to follow logically from what were previously known as conscious facts in combination with certain other facts which were not then consciously perceived but may usually be deduced from the result and fit perfectly into the picture as a whole." (M. R. Wolfard)

"First seek out as many analogies as possible, criticise and eliminate; then examine the small number left by experiment. If this fails begin again with analogies of a quite different type and again follow the process as above. But always analogy is the leading string." (L. W. Andrews)

"I try to think of every possible way of doing a thing and make numerous sketches and descriptions of the various ways as I see them, I finally concentrate on what appears to be the best idea and if the machine or idea admits of it and I have the facilities I make drawings and have working full size machines made which I alter from time to time as a better means appears. If the idea or machine seems impractical and does not perform as I expected I usually discard it and keep my mind and eyes open for a better solution." (R. B. Bryant)

"Practically all my inventions have finally come to me as a flash. It always begins with the creation of need for such improvements, then the study of the problems from all angles, mostly in my mind only, but sometimes with sketches and models. This may take months, or even years—taking it up and laying it down again a number of times—then when alone and at perfect rest, the substantial invention suddenly appears to my mind and immediately I make free-hand sketches and descriptions of what I have. This may not be altogether perfect. The detailed plans, or if this invention consists of a device, experimental work will finish and complete the invention. Further inventions of improvements to the machine, or device, will always follow the experience in actual operation of same." (Samuel Olson)

"Invention may result from innumerable causes, some of which may be matters of chance and others of intent. All inventions I believe to be the result of accumulated observations touched by the imagination into a new thing at sight of a need. An active mind interested in motion and a quick and observant eye perceive in daily life flying birds, running dogs, locomotives, steam and sail boats, and a host of things moving in all sorts of curious ways, suddenly 'discovers' that a bit of work can be done by applying one or more of these curious actions to something a workman is doing by hand, and, Presto! an invention is made.

"I never put problems into words, but deal with them mentally without being conscious of their being expressed in language—when the solution comes in the form of an invention, appearing as it often does in a variety of forms. I analyze them without reducing them to paper and never sketch them until my final choice has been made. Then, when my thoughts stand out like clearly-cut sculptures, I put them on paper, firstly, as a matter of record, and secondly, as a means of describing to my engineers the mechanism I wish constructed for the purpose of putting the invention to work. Formerly I used to sketch out my inventions and clear them up on paper, but I found this to be a slow and cumbersome process and therefore abandoned it.

"It has never been my practice to make models. My first device is always a full-size working mechanism which I intend to be sufficiently complete to be put to use. I never, however, am able to make such a device so complete that it does not require correction and sometimes long experimentation before it is ready for the market. I have often had cases where many inventions have had to be made, in order to accomplish a single result.

"I never let the inventive side of my mind wander outside of the particular matter upon which I am concentrating. I am not an itinerant inventor. Such inventive faculty as I possess I direct as a tool to accomplish the particular results that I desire to achieve. To illustrate my practice in using the inventive faculty as a tool, I cite the case that, being interrupted while I was making a study of the newspaper pressroom by the need first of improving the art of stereotyping, I returned to the newspaper printing press immediately I had finished my work in the stereotyping room. In the end I had succeeded in revolutionizing two departments of the newspaper.

"I am firm in my belief that invention, if it be true invention, is wholly a subconscious reaction to past experiences culminating in the wish to satisfy a need." (Henry A. Wise Wood)

CHAPTER VII

Chance and Accident in Invention

IT IS interesting to note that the word invention is derived from the Latin word *invenire*, which means to come or to light upon. This suggests that there is something of the accidental in invention. This notion is actually held by many people. As a matter of fact, chance or accident plays a very small part in inventing today. We have seen in Chapter VI that the inventors of this study employ deliberate and systematic methods in making their inventions in which chance has a very small part. Only 75 out of 259 inventors who were asked whether chance or accident played any part in their inventing replied in the affirmative. Those who stated that chance played a part in their inventing, however, gave a very narrow and limited meaning to the word chance as we shall see later.

From the strict scientific viewpoint there is no such thing as chance or accident. Every event in nature is strictly predetermined by the events which preceded it. From the viewpoint of a human being, however, with a limited knowledge of all preceding events and with a narrow horizon many things happen which he cannot predict beforehand. When such an unforeseen event occurs we say it happens by chance or accident, and if this occurrence is to the advantage of some individual we call it luck.

Many impressive and highly colored stories have been told of accidental discoveries and inventions. It is natural, of course, that such stories should appeal to the popular imagination, for they are intensely dramatic. A careful study of these stories of accidental inventions, however, will reveal the fact that lucky accidents only happen to those who deserve them.

In nearly all cases we find that the accident happens only after a persistent and carefully conducted search for what is wanted. Undoubtedly man's earliest discoveries and inventions were the result of pure chance. His urge to manipulate and to explore the objects of his environment caused him to stumble upon many new facts which he utilized in satisfying his wants. We can readily see that these accidental discoveries were made without any purpose or foresight. We must remember, however, that accident alone is not sufficient to produce the invention. In all such cases, as E. Mach has said, "The inventor is obliged to take note of the new fact, he must discover and grasp its advantageous feature, and must have the power to turn that feature to account in the realization of his purpose. He must distinguish the new feature, impress it upon his memory, unite and interweave it with the rest of his thought, in short, he must possess the capacity to profit by experience." [1]

The accident merely gives the inventor the necessary elements out of which to make his invention, or it may give him a clue for the solution of his problem. However, the inventor must first experience or recognize a need before he can invent. The passive observation of an accident can never lead to an invention. It is only when an accidental event is perceived and mentally manipulated to complete a pattern or to formulate a new relationship that an invention can be made. We can readily see that accidental events could occur for thousands of years before the eyes of man without a single invention being made. Man, for instance, had seen broken tree limbs and trunks floating on water for many years before it occurred to him that he could make a boat. Primitive man probably observed for thousands of years that the heat of the sun could bake moist mud or clay into a hard mass,

[1] E. Mach, On the part played by accident in invention and discovery, Monist, 1896, 6, 161-175.

but it was necessary for the primitive inventor not only to observe this but also to appreciate its practical possibilities and to utilize this discovery to make pottery.

Chance or accident thus is merely one of the ways of obtaining facts which can be applied for inventive purposes. Primitive man having a small fund of knowledge and guided chiefly by empirical methods had to rely largely on chance for supplying the necessary elements needed for his inventions. Modern man, however, has built up a vast cultural fund of knowledge which is passed on from generation to generation. With the increase of knowledge and with the development of the scientific method the inventor today rarely invents by chance alone. Of course, problems often arise which defy all possible attempts at solution. The inventor may spend years in finding the proper combination which will meet the difficulty.

It is often by accident that he may get a subtle clue. As Mach says: "We have to wait for the appearance of a favorable physical accident. The movement of our thoughts obeys the law of association. In the case of meagre experience the result of this law is simply the mechanical reproduction of definite sensory experiences. On the other hand, if the physical life is subjected to the incessant influences of a powerful and rich experience, then every representative element in the mind is connected with so many others that the actual and natural course of thoughts is easily influenced and determined by insignificant circumstances, which accidently are decisive. Hereupon, the process termed imagination produces its protean and infinitely diversified forms." [2]

We have seen that the mental process of invention depends to a great extent on mental trial and error, which eventually terminates in a satisfactory solution. Inasmuch as the exact procedure is not known and the solution cannot be foreseen in the beginning we might say

[2] E. Mach, On the part played by accident in invention and discovery, Monist, 1896, 6, 171.

that the solution is obtained by chance. We must attribute to chance the formation of a satisfactory mental pattern from the innumerable mental elements derived from the inventor's past experience. Souriau [3] in his book *Theorie de l'Invention* has been considerably impressed by this phase of the accidental in our mental processes and he finally concludes that chance is the first principle of invention. According to Souriau, when a problem is given to us for solution, we do not know what ideas to follow. We know with what series our thoughts must end, but we do not know how to begin. In this case, it is evident that we must begin by chance. Our mind goes on the first path open before it, and after perceiving that it is a false one, will follow other paths until it arrives at the desired idea. Under these conditions we are forced to take account of chance.

In this chapter, however, we are not concerned with the element of chance in our mental processes but with chance occurrences in the environment of the inventor leading him to invent. As far as our surroundings are concerned chance does not produce inventions. It only determines whether this or that individual shall make an invention and not whether the particular invention shall be made. Chance is the outcome of unknown events or circumstances. When the chance event occurs the inventor recognizes its significance and he will immediately make practical use of it. In this sense accidents happen only to those that deserve them because they set the scene so that when an accident happens they are capable of recognizing its significance and benefiting thereby.

It frequently happens that while an inventor is engaged in making an invention he will stumble over some facts for which he was not looking. It is well known that this often happens to workers in many different fields. This lucky find is termed "serendipity" after the Persian god of chance. It is really "accidental sagacity." The

[3] P. Souriau, Theorie de l'invention, Paris, Libraire Hatchette, 1881.

inventor in making an accidental observation of this kind must not only note what occurs but he must also see the possibility of applying what he observes for a useful and practical purpose. Before the invention of the microscope, for instance, many people observed that dew drops on leaves acted as a magnifying glass bringing out the details of the veins beneath, but it took the insight of an inventor to apply this observation to a practical purpose. It has often been said that the prototypes of many of our inventions are found in nature, and that all our inventions are copies of mechanism found in nature. Even assuming that this is true, which is improbable, it is strange that it took thousands of years for man to appreciate the applicability of the mechanism he saw in nature for his own use. Actually as George Iles says: "While inventors in the past might have taken many a hint from nature, as a matter of fact they seldom did so, but went ahead, hit-or-miss, failing to observe that what they reached with much laborious fumbling, often they might have copied directly from nature."[4]

"Many a time have designers and inventors paralleled, without knowing it, some structure of nature often seen but never really observed. All the variety and beauty of the Greek orders of architecture failed to include the arch; yet the contour of every architect's own skull was all the while displaying an arched form which could lend to temple and palace new strength as well as grace. The skeleton of the foot reveals in the instep an arch of tarsal and metatarsal bones, with all the springiness which their possessor may confer upon composite arch of wood or steel. Modern builders, whether wittingly or not, have taken a leaf from the book of nature in rearing their tallest structures with hollow cylinders of steel. What is this but borrowing the form of the reed, the bamboo, a thousand varieties of stalk, one of the strongest shapes in which supporting material can be disposed? Pass a knife

---

[4] G. Iles, Inventors at work, New York, Doubleday, 1906, 267.

across a blade of pipe or moor grass and you will find a hollow cylinder stayed by buttresses numbering nearly a score." [5]

"Long before there was a philosopher to classify levers into distinct kinds, the foot of man was afforded examples of levers of the first and second orders, and his forearm of a lever of the third order. Ages before the crudest bagpipe was put together, the lungs by which they were to be blown, and the larynx joined to those lungs, were displaying a wind instrument of perfect model. The wrists, ankles, and vertebrae of Hooke might well have served him in designing his universal joint. Indeed weapons, tools, instruments, machines, and engines are, after all, but extensions and modified copies of the bodily organs of the inventor himself." [6]

Primitive man, even modern man, has not utilized many of the things occurring in nature for making inventions because mere observation never makes an invention. We may observe events or occurrences which chance to happen before us but to utilize these in the form of an invention requires insight, imagination, and all the inventive processes of an inventor.

The story is frequently told that Newton discovered the law of gravitation upon observing an apple fall; that Galileo made his pendulum after observing the swinging of a chandelier in a cathedral; that Watt made his steam-engine upon seeing the oscillations of the lid of a steam-kettle. These stories are probably pure fiction. Newton did not discover "the attraction of gravitation." What he discovered was that the same force which caused a stone or an apple to fall to the earth when left unsupported, also retained the moon in her orbit. He proved this by comparing the rate of falling bodies on the earth with the rate at which the moon deviated from the straight line which she would have pursued if the earth did not exist.

---

[5] G. Iles, Inventors at work, New York, Doubleday, 1906, 250-251.
[6] Ibid., 256.

As stated by Phin: "Galileo had long been engaged in investigations relating to falling bodies and had fully proved the absolute regularity of their motion when he suggested the use of the pendulum as a time measurer. Very probably he may have watched the swinging chandelier and used it as an illustration, but it was his previous studies and earnest thought and not the mere swinging of the chandelier that pointed to the utility of the pendulum." [7]

Watt's story is highly improbable because the power of steam was known long before Watt was born and before tea-kettles were in general use. Steam-engines were also in existence when he invented his steam-engine.

Another improbable story is the accidental discovery of glass as told by the Roman author Tacitus, which has been repeated by many writers. According to his story some Phoenician mariners were shipwrecked near the mouth of the Belus river. They built a fire on the beach using some limestones to support their fuel. The sand combined with the limestone under the heat of the fire producing glass. This story is probably unfounded as the heat produced in the open air would be insufficient to fuse the materials entering into the composition of glass. The origin of glass actually dates back not less than three thousand years before the Christian era. It was known to the Egyptians many centuries before our time. An Egyptian tomb has been found having a painting showing two glass-blowers who are seated on each side of a lighted furnace and have in their hands blow-pipes which are used for blowing molten glass.

Although most of the stories relating to accidental inventions and discoveries are pure fiction yet there are some genuine examples of accidental inventions of record. A few interesting cases will be given.

One of the best-known cases of accidental discoveries is that of the vulcanization of rubber. Goodyear was ex-

[7] J. Phin, Seven follies of science, New York, Van Nostrand, 1912, 180.

perimenting for many years in the attempt to vulcanize rubber but he met with no success. One day as he was mixing a batch of rubber with sulphur a small portion of his mix fell on a hot stove. The heat vulcanized the rubber at once. Goodyear immediately saw the solution to his problem which had baffled him for many years and reduced him to poverty and despair.

Commenting on this accident he said: "I was for many years seeking to accomplish this object, and allowing nothing to escape my notice that related to it. Like the falling apple before Newton's gaze, it was suggestive of an important fact to one whose mind was previously prepared to draw an inference from any occurrence which might favor the object of his research. While I admit that these discoveries of mine were not the result of scientific chemical investigation, I am not willing to admit that they are the result of what is commonly called accident. I claim them to be the result of the closest application and observation." [8]

The remarkable sweetening power of saccharine was accidentally discovered by a chemist who happened to eat his lunch in the laboratory without washing his hands after performing some experiments. Some chemical on his fingers gave his sandwich an unusually sweet taste. An investigation of the various materials which he just handled led him to discover saccharine as the cause of the sweetness.

In 1876 Dr. Elihu Thomson was demonstrating to his class the effects of centrifugal force and its useful applications in the steam-engine governor, centrifugal drying machines and centrifugal draining machines in sugar refineries. During his lecture demonstration he happened to whirl a bottle having some sediment in it and he noticed that the sediment settled promptly to the outside of the bottle. It occurred to him then that centrifugal force could be used to separate liquids of different density

[8] G. Iles, Leading American inventors, New York, Holt, 1912, 192.

in the same manner. This led to the development of the centrifugal cream separator which is now used everywhere. The presence of the sediment in the bottle used by Dr. Thomson was of course an accident. Dr. Thomson, however, had to observe what happened to the sediment, noticed the significance of this occurrence and realized its applicability for practical purposes. He then made several experiments and devised apparatus to test out his conception. The same accident happening to another man would probably never have led to the invention of the centrifugal cream separator.

A great step in the development of photography was made by Daguerre accidentally when he left an exposed photographic plate in a closet which happened to contain an open dish of mercury. Next morning he noticed much to his surprise that the image was developed on the plate. He surmised that this was caused by some substance in the closet and after looking around he found that it was due to the mercury vapors given off from the dish on the shelf. This led to the establishment of "developers" in photography. This discovery was, of course, accidental but we must remember that Daguerre had been working for a long time on photography and as a consequence he was prepared to take note of all occurrences which might be useful to him in his work.

The use of nutgall solution as a photographic developer was discovered by Talbot when it came in contact accidentally with some exposed photographic paper. Thus very often the opportunity of observation comes by accident. The occurrence is not sought for or deliberately arranged, but the inventor will at once perceive the significance of the accidental occurrence and embody the principles he discovers in a practical invention.

Becquerel discovered that uranium gives off invisible rays by putting some of it in a drawer containing a photographic plate. Later he noticed that an image was formed on the plate although it was never exposed. This led to an investigation of the radiation of uranium.

The manufacture of synthetic indigo from naphthalene was a baffling problem to chemists. A search was made for a catalyst which would bring about the desired oxidation but no suitable catalyst could be found. One day a thermometer immersed in the apparatus broke causing the mercury to run out. The desired chemical reaction took place at once due to the mercury. Of course, if the experiments were conducted for a sufficient length of time mercury would probably have been tried. However, the actual discovery was made by accident.

The offset method of printing was due to the failure of a feeder of a lithographic machine to place a sheet of paper in position at the right moment so that it did not pass through the machine. The work on the printing surface left its full impression upon the printing cylinder, and when the next sheet passed through, it received an impression from the printing surface while an indirect or set-off print was made from the back upon the paper. The effects of this accident were observed by Ira W. Rufel who happened to stand nearby leading him to the invention of offset printing. Very often the fault of a workman or an accidental misfortune may lead to a new invention.

"At the General Motors research laboratories they had been wondering for a long time why automobile engines under certain conditions knocked. The cause was easily traced to the fuel, and someone in the Laboratories conceived the idea that if the color of the fuel were properly changed the engine might stop knocking. The theory proved ultimately to be entirely wrong, but here is what happened. The member of the staff who conceived this bright idea went to the chemical storeroom and asked for a coloring material that would completely dissolve in gasoline. The storekeeper did not know offhand of any such material, but when he looked over the shelves his glance fell on a bottle of iodine and he handed that out in the belief that iodine would dissolve in the gasoline and would certainly give it a color. As the experimenter did not know what color, if any, would produce the desired effect, he tried iodine, with the result that the knocking disappeared.

"Now, out of some 10,000 bottles in the storeroom of the Laboratories, there was just one bottle that contained a material that would eliminate knocking, and that was the bottle containing the iodine and purely by chance was this particular material tried out of the thousands of materials available. The successful performance of iodine made it possible to develop the true theory of knocking, and this in its turn led to the discovery of anti-detonants, which promises to revolutionize the design of automobile and airplane." [9]

The discovery of X-rays was due to an accident. Professor Roentgen was working in a photographic darkroom, in which there was a barium-platino-cyanide plate. When the Crooke's tube was worked in an adjoining room the barium-platino-cyanide in the dark room became luminous. Roentgen concluded that some invisible radiation passed through the wall and entered the barium-platino-cyanide. This led to the discovery of X-rays. Of course, the discovery was a fluke but very few people would have had the imagination or energy to follow it up.

Mr. Henry A. Wise Wood said: "Chance or accident has played a part in my inventing to the extent only which the following will illustrate: It was *chance* that took me into the printing machinery business. Because I was interested in movement and my tastes were mechanical my mind *gravitated* to the mechanical side of that business. I *chanced* one day to see a man wreck a machine through improperly using it. I thereupon invented a mechanism which made it fool-proof. I *happened* to be present when an accident occurred to a man which caused the loss of his finger in the operation of a machine. I thereupon invented a means which would render impossible repetition of the accident. I *chanced* to notice that in machines for smoothing the interior of printing plates

[9] Anon., Accidental discoveries, Mechanical Engineering, 1926, 48, 865.

the resulting chips would continue to lie in the machine and injure the following plate unless carefully removed by hand. I turned the machine upside down so that the chips would drop out of their own accord, thus inventing a means of overcoming a persistent cause of trouble."

The first aniline dye made from coal-tar was made accidentally by Perkin in the course of some experiments in which he was attempting to make quinine from coal-tar. At the end of an unsuccessful experiment Perkin obtained a black mess which he was about to throw out, but before doing so he added some alcohol and there flashed before him a beautiful purple color, the first coal-tar dye.

The manufacture of dynamite by Alfred Nobel was due to an accidental leak of a nitroglycerin can. The liquid explosive was absorbed by the porous sand in which the cans were packed and it hardened into a solid mass. It was at this time that Nobel was in great difficulty over the transportation of the new explosive. A steamship loaded with nitroglycerin bound from Hamburg to Chili was blown up in mid-ocean. Railroad trains met with a similar fate. Three years before, Nobel's factory at Helensborg had been wrecked with the loss of his youngest brother's life. This conversion of nitroglycerin into a solid by absorption in porous earth saved the day for high explosives and led Nobel to the invention of dynamite which is a comparatively safe explosive.

The accidental invention of lithography is described by Senfelder, its inventor, in his own words as follows: "I had just succeeded in polishing a stone plate, which I intended to cover with etching-ground, in order to continue my exercise in writing backwards, when my mother entered the room and desired me to write her a bill for the washerwoman, who was waiting for the linen. I happened not to have even the smallest slip of paper at hand, as my little stock of paper had been entirely exhausted by taking proof impressions from the stones; nor was there even a drop of ink in the inkstand. As the matter would not admit of delay, and we had nobody in the house to send for a supply of the deficient materials, I resolved to write the list with my ink prepared with wax, soap, and lamp-black, on the stone which I had just polished, and from which I could copy it at leisure. Some time after this, I was just going to wipe this writing from the stone, when the idea all at once struck me to try what would be the effect of such a writing with my prepared ink if I were to bite in the stone with aqua fortis; and, having bitten away to abcut the hundredth part of an inch, I found that I could charge the lines with printing ink, and take successive impressions." [10]

Goodyear's discovery of the vulcanization of rubber and the other illustrations given support the conclusion that accidents happened only to those that deserved them. Goodyear did not discover the vulcanization of rubber just by pure inspiration of imagination. He worked hard for many years trying the effect of many chemicals on raw rubber and if it were not for these experiments, although unsuccessful in themselves, he would never have discovered the vulcanization of rubber.

The clue to a baffling problem may often come by pure chance either while conducting experiments or by a chance occurrence in some entirely unrelated field. The inventor's mind acts like a very sensitive selective apparatus seizing at once any suggestions arising from chance events that occur which can be utilized in solving his problem.

These illustrations also show that chance very often supplies the facts to an inventor which he utilizes for making his invention. Daguerre found by chance that mercury vapors could be used as a developer. Similarly Talbot found by accident that a solution of nutgalls was a good developer. In all these accidental cases, however, we must remember that the alert mind and keen observation of the inventor were highly essential before an invention could be possibly made. The same accidents happen-

---

[10] J. Burnley, The romance of invention, London, Cassell, 1892, 140.

ing before other people would, even if observed, produce no direct consequences. The inventor, on the other hand, appreciates the significance and the importance of the chance occurrence and utilizes it for practical purposes.

CHAPTER VIII

MULTIPLE INVENTION

ONE OF THE most interesting aspects of invention is that the minds of many inventors run in the same channel, so to speak. Year after year there are thousands of inventions which are re-invented. The Patent Office records show that a little more than half of the applications filed for patents ever mature into patents. The remaining applications are rejected chiefly because patents have been previously obtained for the same inventions by other inventors. It seems that when the same obstacles are presented to different people they will ultimately find a similar solution of the difficulty. This is, of course, a natural and expected happening. Given the same problem and the mechanical elements and physical limitations the number of possible practical solutions are limited and different people will, therefore, arrive at similar conclusions under such circumstances.

In these cases of re-invention there is usually a considerable lapse of time between the original invention and its re-invention by some other inventor. Many instances, however, occur where the inventions are made practically simultaneously by different individuals who have never communicated with each other and who live in remotely scattered parts of the world. A surprisingly large number of our great inventions and discoveries have been made by different individuals at about the same time. For this reason it is often very difficult to determine who is the actual first inventor. At any given level of our technical development and knowledge, certain problems will arise which could not have arisen before. The elements to solve these problems are found in the existing fund of knowledge and experience. Since the workers in any given field have the same common cultural background it follows that the current problems will direct them to the same solution.

When the same patentable invention is made by two or more inventors who attempt to obtain patents in the Patent Office a proceeding is instituted to determine the question of priority of the invention. This proceeding is designated as an "interference." It is one of the most complicated legal proceedings in existence. The inventors present their testimony and exhibits and the Patent Office officials finally decide which inventor is entitled to the patent.

Very often there are more than two inventions involved in an interference. There is one interference on record which involved over fifty individuals. In this case the Patent Office dismissed the entire proceeding, deciding with the wisdom of a Solomon that no invention could possibly be present where so many individuals could suggest the same solution to a problem.

There were over 1800 interferences instituted in 1929 in the United States Patent Office. The following table gives the actual number of interferences for the last seven years.

TABLE 4

ANNUAL NUMBER OF INTERFERENCES IN THE U. S. PATENT OFFICE

Year	No. of Interferences	Total Applications Filed	Per cent of Applications
1923	1744	79,058	2.2
1924	1583	80,756	1.9
1925	1581	84,525	1.8
1926	1604	86,028	1.8
1927	1599	92,018	1.7
1928	1728	92,598	1.9
1929	1806	94,489	1.9

It is apparent that such a large number of simultaneous inventions cannot be the result of pure chance. Table 4 shows that the number of interferences instituted each year in the United States Patent Office amounts to about

2 per cent of all the patent applications filed each year. As each interference involves at least two applications it means that about 4 per cent of all patent applications filed each year contain multiple inventions.

We have seen in the last chapter that inventions are the result of unsatisfied needs and when these needs are recognized by more than one inventor it is inevitable that simultaneous inventions will occur. Two important conditions, however, must be satisfied before any invention can be made after a need for it has been recognized. We must, first, have the necessary technical development or background which will supply all the necessary elements for the invention and second, we must have the inventor to make the invention from the known existing elements. The unsatisfied fundamental human needs are more likely to cause multiple inventions than the needs which are not so urgent and which cause no great inconvenience in remaining unsatisfied. Many inventions could have been made centuries ago as far as technical requirements were concerned but they were not made because no inventive individual saw the possibility of a new configuration of known physical facts or perceived a new relationship which would lead him to make an invention. The invention of the phonograph by Edison is a good illustration in point. For more than a century eminent physicists were studying sound and recording speech vibrations by means of the vibrograph, which was a diaphragm carrying a point resting against a cylinder carrying a strip of smoked paper to record sound waves, but it never occurred to any one of them to run it backwards. Edison, however, heard a peculiar sound made by a rough strip of paper used in a telegraphic apparatus and immediately made an apparatus to reproduce sound.[1]

It is possible to have the necessary cultural development containing all the requisite elements for a needed invention and yet the invention will not be made because

[1] See R. A. Fessenden, The deluged civilization, Boston, T. J. Russell Print, 1923, 101-102.

the need has not been experienced by an individual who has the proper emotional reaction and knowledge to cause him to invent. This situation, especially where fundamental human needs are involved, does not continue very long because, as we have seen, the psychological processes of invention are found to a more or less extent in all human individuals and according to the laws of probability there will be more than one individual in a large group who possesses the necessary emotional reaction to the need. It follows, therefore, that inventions are inevitable at certain levels of our cultural development. The large number of multiple independent inventions is strong evidence in favor of this view.

We thus see that necessity alone is not the mother of invention if the essential elements for an invention do not exist. "However, if the necessary constituent elements exist, the invention may occur if there is a cultural need for it, for at any one time the distribution of inherent mental ability is such that in a large sample there are many cases of exceptional native mental ability." [2] In proof of this statement Ogburn and Thomas have made a list of 148 important inventions and discoveries which have been made independently by two or more persons. A few of the interesting cases are given at the end of this chapter. Stern [3] has also compiled a list containing over 150 important multiple discoveries and inventions in medicine made independently by two or more persons. Practically every important advance in medicine will be found in this list.

Most of us have been taught to attribute the origin of an invention to a definite and known individual. The public loves to worship heroes in all walks of life and this is particularly true of inventors. Many of the popular stories of inventions appeal very greatly to the imagi-

---

[2] W. F. Ogburn and D. Thomas, Are inventions inevitable? Political Science Quarterly, 1922, 37, 83-98.

[3] B. J. Stern, Social factors in medical progress, New York, Columbia Univ. Press, 1927, 111-127.

nation. The biographers of the famous inventors have been chiefly responsible for stressing the genius of their inventors as the sole cause of their inventions. This is the heroic theory of invention which asserts "that without the one man whose life they are chronicling, a particular invention could not, or would not readily have been forthcoming." [4]

An analysis, however, of the history of any highly developed invention shows that it is extremely difficult to assign it to a single individual. Inventions are seldom the work of a single mind. The history of the steamship is a good example in point. Most school children are taught that Fulton invented the steamship. Actually we find that "the utility of the steamship was perceived by Homer, who sang of the marvelous, great, black ships of the Phoenicians, which without sail or oar or crew, sped swiftly to the remotest ends of earth, bringing back merchandise. Next, paddle-wheels descend from Roman days. In the thirteenth century Roger Bacon, from his experiments with gunpowder, glimpsed the internal combustion engine, and the means of fulfilling the Homeric desire. He wrote 'Art can construct instruments of navigation such that the largest vessels, governed by a single man, will traverse rivers and seas more rapidly than if they were filled with oarsmen.' A steamboat had probably been suggested by 1651, and built by 1738, and we have patents with descriptions of 1729 and 1736. But no success was to be expected from such craft, for their engines were wretched. Watt's double-acting expansive steam-engine appeared in 1782 and the next year the Marquis de Jouffroy had built a great boat, not fast enough, at Lyons. Before the end of the century steamboats had been built by many inventors especially Rumsey on the Potomac and Thames, Fitch on the Delaware, who realized good speed and long commercial use, and by Evans, and Miller, who in 1789 made 6 knots on the Forth

[4] See R. C. Epstein, Industrial invention, heroic or systematic? Quarterly Journal of Economics, 1926, 40, 232-272.

& Clyde Canal. In 1802 on the same water Symington's *Charlotte Dundas* was a perfect success, save that she washed down the canal's banks. Presently John Stevens, of Hoboken, had speedy steam yachts on the Hudson, even with twin screws, tubular boilers and high pressure, excellent save for the damning workmanship in their motive plant.

"Meanwhile Fulton, as we know from direct testimony, had been studying the plans of boats, and interviewing the designers, of every one of the important previous projects, in France, England and America. So had the other inventors been studying, the steamboat evolving out of joint experience; but none were so assiduous as Fulton. In all about thirty steamboats had been built, all in those three countries, generally in the order given. Fulton first built a 66-foot boat on the Seine at Paris, and obtained some speed, but little attention and no success. So he returned to the great rivers of America, and in 1807 launched the *Clermont* in the Hudson, and steamed for Albany at 5 miles per hour.

"The chief reason for this confusion of parentage is that the process of making a great invention is totally different from the common understanding about it. A great invention is not a completed product, issuing at one time from the brain of one inventor. It is a multitudinous collection of little inventions and is a growth of centuries. Had a single inventor to make the whole, he would need more hands than a monkey, more lives than a cat and more inventive genius than Pallas, Hermes and Loki combined."[5]

This view has been expressed by nearly all students of the history of inventions. We not only inherit our biological structure from our ancestors but also the cultural structure created by them. Our civilization is the result of small accretions of achievement to the culture which we find when we are born. It is our ability to change

[5] S. C. Giltillan, Who invented it? Sci. Monthly, 1927, 25, 529-534.

and modify our culture and environment which has given us our great faith and belief in progress. It has, therefore, been said that the human race is the true inventor. This view does not necessarily disparage the importance of the individual inventor, for all improvements and progress in existing inventions must be made through the individual inventor.

Smiles states in this connection "rarely does it happen that any discovery or invention of importance is made by one man alone. The threads of inquiry are taken up and traced, one labourer succeeding another, each tracing it a little further, often without apparent result. This goes on sometimes for centuries, until at length some man, greater perhaps than his fellows, seeking to fulfill the needs of his time, gathers the various threads together, treasures up the gain of past successes and failures, and uses them as the means for some solid achievement.

"The arts are indeed reared but slowly; and it was a wise observation of Lord Bacon that we are too apt to pass those ladders by which they have been reared, and reflect the whole merit on the last new performer. Thus, what is hailed as an original invention is often found to be but the result of a long succession of trials and experiments gradually following each other, which ought rather to be considered as a continuous series of achievements of the human mind than as the conquest of any single individual. It has sometimes taken centuries of experience to ascertain the value of a single fact in its various bearings. Like man himself, experience is feeble and apparently purposeless in its infancy, but acquires maturity and strength with age. Experience, however, is not limited to a lifetime, but is the stored-up wealth and power of our race. Even amidst the death of successive generations it is constantly advancing and accumulating, exhibiting at the same time the weakness and the power, the littleness and the greatness of our common humanity." [6]

---

[6] S. Smiles, Industrial biography, London, John Murray, 1884, 169.

We have seen that actual evidence indicates that the same inventions are frequently made independently by two or more men. We must remember, however, that in such cases these persons were faced with the similar problem and that they had the same cultural background. Do we have any records of inventions which have been made by individuals in different cultural periods and in two different parts of the world? The words of Solomon "The thing that hath been is that which shall be, and there is no new thing under the sun" have often been quoted. There seems to be some inconclusive evidence that the same inventions have been made by individuals in widely different historic periods. It is often stated for instance that the Chinese invented paper making, printing, and gunpowder, long before these were invented by the Europeans.

According to a recent work [7] on printing the invention of paper made from bark, hemp, old rags and fish nets was officially announced in 105 B. C. The earliest extant paper dating back to 150 B. C. was found by Stern in a spur of the Great Chinese Wall. There were three elevators used in the palace of the Cæsars. Hero invented a coin-in-the-slot machine. The money deposited in this machine actuated a valve causing a flow of water to be used for religious purposes.[8]

Fournier [9] states that the lightning-rod was known to the ancient Jews and that Solomon's temple was protected by lightning-rods. Wood was made incombustible by the ancients by impregnating it with alum. The Hindoos used the virus of cow-pox for centuries before Jenner. All these inventions are, of course, supposed to be modern inventions. Many more examples could be given.

---

[7] T. F. Carter, The invention of printing in China, New York, Columbia Univ. Press, 1925.

[8] H. E. Dudeney, Antiquity of modern inventions, Strand, 1913, 45, 446-450.

[9] E. Fournier, Le vieux-neuf, Paris, E. Dentu, 1877, Vol. 1, 170, 176, 268-269.

According to Smiles "coal-gas was regularly used by the Chinese for lighting purposes long before it was known amongst us. Hydropathy was generally practiced by the Romans, who established baths wherever they went. Even chloroform is no new thing. The use of ether as an anæsthetic was known to Albertus Magnus, who flourished in the thirteenth century; and in his works he gives a recipe for its preparation. In 1681 Denis Papin published his 'Traite des Operations sans Douleur,' showing that he had discovered methods of deadening pain. But the use of anæsthetics is much older than Albertus Magnus or Papin; for the ancients had their nepenthe and mandragora; the Chinese their mayo, and the Egyptians their hachisch (both preparations of Cannabis Indica)." [10]

"The balloon was an ancient Italian invention, revived by Montgolfier long after the original had been forgotten. Even the reaping-machine is an old invention revived. Thus Barnabe Googe, the translator of a book from the German entitled 'The Whole Arts and Trade of Husbandrie,' published in 1577, in the reign of Elizabeth, speaks of the reaping-machine as a worn-out invention—a thing 'which was woont to be used in France. The device was a lowe kinde of carre with a couple of wheeles, and the frunt armed with sharpe syckles, which, forced by the beaste through the corne, did cut down all before it. This tricke,' says Googe, 'might be used in levell and champion countreys; but with us it wolde make but ill-favoured worke.' The Thames Tunnel was thought an entirely new manifestation of engineering genius; but the tunnel under the Euphrates at ancient Babylon, and that under the wide mouth of the harbour at Marseilles (a much more difficult work), show that the ancients were beforehand with us in the art of tunnelling. Macadamized roads are as old as the Roman empire; and suspen-

[10] Smiles, Industrial biography, London, John Murray, 1884, 174.

sion bridges, though comparatively new in Europe, have been known in China for centuries." [11]

Smiles relies largely on Fournier's "Le Vieux-Neuf" for his sources of information. We must always remember that many of the statements made in ancient literature are mere expressions of desired inventions rather than statements of inventions actually in existence and we must, therefore, not be misled into accepting these statements as positive statements as to the actual existence of these inventions. Many of these statements, however, have been accepted by the uncritical as statements of facts, for which no actual proof can be found or is known. They should at best be taken with "a grain of salt."

The question of independent inventions has been given considerable thought by modern anthropologists. The tools and remains of prehistoric man in different parts of the world have been carefully studied in order to see whether they were independently evolved or whether they had a common origin. Two theories have been consequently developed to explain what they found. One school of anthropologists follows the diffusion theory of culture which states that once an invention was made it diffused over the globe and was adopted in time by diverse peoples. Some astonishing similarities in culture have been found in widely scattered parts of the world which can of course be easily explained by diffusion. In some cases, however, it is difficult to see just how an invention could possibly diffuse to an inaccessible and remote part of the world. The independent origin of the inventions has been accordingly advocated by many anthropologists to explain this phenomenon.

When we consider that the physical laws of nature have been constant as far back as we know and that the human being has been using the same mental processes in all parts of the world and experiencing the same needs,

---

[11] Smiles, Industrial biography, London, John Murray, 1884, 173.

it would not be surprising to see the same inventions made in different historic periods having different cultures. However, such multiple inventions can be possible only for the simplest types of inventions satisfying basic human needs. We could not, of course, expect to find a complicated television or radio invention in Babylonian times because they did not have a cultural development similar to ours. However, when it comes to the simple necessities of life such as household utensils, clothing and shelter we are bound to have multiple inventions because similar and often identical materials were used and the needs are the same universally.

The following table gives a list of some interesting multiple inventions and discoveries selected from a table compiled by Ogburn and Thomas.[12]

[12] W. F. Ogburn and D. Thomas, Are inventions inevitable? Political Science Quarterly, 1922, 37, 93-98.

TABLE 5

A LIST OF SOME INVENTIONS AND DISCOVERIES MADE INDEPENDENTLY BY TWO OR MORE PERSONS

Discovery of the planet Neptune	By Adams (1845) and Leverrier (1845)
Logarithms	By Burgi (1620) and Napier-Briggs (1614)
Calculus	By Newton (1671) and Leibnitz (1676)
Discovery of oxygen	By Scheele (1774) and Priestley (1774)
Liquefaction of oxygen	By Cailletet (1877) and Pictet (1877)
Method of liquefying gases	By Cailletet, Pictet, Wroblowski and Olzewski (all between 1877 and 1884)
Molecular theory	By Ampere (1814) and Avagadro (1811)
Process for reduction of aluminum	By Hall (1886), Heroult (1887) and Cowles (1885)
Photography	By Daguerre-Niepe (1839) and Talbot (1839)
Kinetic theory of gases	By Clausius (1850) and Rankine (1850)
Mechanical equivalent of heat	By Mayer (1842), Carnot (1830), Seguin (1839) and Joule (1840)
Pneumatic lever	By Hamilton (1835) and Barker (1832)
Telegraph	By Henry (1831), Morse (1837), Cooke-Wheatstone (1837) and Steinheil (1837)
Electric motors	By Dal Negro (1830), Henry (1831), Bourbonze and McGawley (1835)
Electric railroad	Claimed by Davidson, Jacobi, Lilly-Colton (1847), Davenport (1835), Page (1850) and Hall (1850-1)
Ring armature	By Pacinotti (1864) and Gramme (1860)
Microphone	Hughes (1878), Edison (1877-8), Berliner (1877) and Blake (1878)
Telephone	By Bell (1876) and Gray (1876)
Theory of the infection of micro-organisms	By Fracastoro (1546) and Kircher
Relation of micro-organisms to fermentation and putrefaction	By Latour (1837) and Schwann (1837)
Laws of heredity	By Mendel (1865), De Vries (1900), Correns (1900) and Tschermarck (1900)
Balloon	By Montgolfier (1783), Rittenhouse-Hopkins (1783)
Flying machine	By Wright (1895-1901), Langley (1893-7) and others
Reapers	By Hussey (1833) and McCormick (1834)
Double-flanged rail	By Stevens and Vignolet
Cylinder printing press	By Koenig-Bensley (1812-13) and Napier (1830)
Typewriter	By Beach (1847-56), Sholes? (1872) and Wheatstone (1855-60)
Trolley car	By Van Doeple (1884-85), Sprague (1888), Siemens (1881) and Daft (1883)
Centrifugal pumps	By Appold (1850), Gwynne (1850), and Bessemer (1850)

CHAPTER IX

The Occupation of the Inventor

IT IS surprising that most of the great and revolutionary inventions were made by men whom we would least expect to make inventions today. Richard Arkwright, the inventor of the spinning-frame, was a barber; Edmund Cartwright, the inventor of the power-loom, was a clergyman; James Watt, the inventor of the improved steam-engine, was a maker of scientific instruments; Robert Fulton, famed for his steamboat, was a portrait painter; Eli Whitney, the inventor of the cotton-gin, was a lawyer; Morse, the inventor of the telegraph, was a landscape painter; Bell, who is identified with the telephone, was a teacher of deaf-mutes; J. and W. Hyatt, inventors of celluloid, were printers; William Armstrong, the inventor of the hydraulic engine, was a lawyer. Many other instances could be given.

We must remember that in the days of the inventors just mentioned technical knowledge was very limited. There were no mechanical experts and technical specialists as we have today. These inventors undoubtedly had an intense urge to contrive, as well as the love of tinkering with mechanical devices. A review of the careers of the great inventors shows that they had a decided bent towards mechanics early in life, as well as the capacity for drudgerous detail and prolonged intense effort. These men, therefore, invented in spite of their daily occupation. They could also obtain with a comparatively little effort all the technical knowledge existing in their time.

Today, not only has our technical knowledge increased tremendously but men have also specialized to a much greater extent, particularly in the engineering fields, so that it would be almost impossible for any individual to master all the extant knowledge even in a specialized field.

For this reason great inventions are seldom made today by barbers, clergymen, artists or lawyers. Our technical knowledge has increased to such a great extent that we can hardly expect to see our future revolutionary inventors coming from men employed in non-technical fields. It is, of course, true that basic inventions have been made in the past by men who had little or no technical knowledge. We might ask why didn't a farmer invent the reaping machine? Why wasn't the automobile invented by carriage makers or by a locomotive engineman? We should naturally expect to have the automobile invented by someone engaged in transportation. Why didn't a dressmaker or a tailor invent the sewing-machine, instead of leaving the task to Howe, the machinist? Why didn't some road engineer, or quarry owner, or mine superintendent, invent the rock crusher, instead of Blake, the manufacturer of hardware? Why didn't a professor of physics or an electrical engineer invent the telephone, instead of Bell, the teacher of deaf and dumb pupils? Why didn't a southern planter, or a mill owner, or a mechanic, invent the cotton-gin, instead of Whitney, the lawyer?

The reason for this peculiar lack of correlation of occupation and type of invention can be explained on several grounds. We must remember that a man inexperienced in a given field often has a distinct advantage over the men who are experienced in that field. First of all, he has nothing to lose, for his professional reputation is not at stake. He also tackles his problem without any preconceived notions or theories. He is, therefore, free to formulate his own theories or possible solutions of the problem. He is not bound by any precedent in that field and he respects no authorities, because he is ignorant of the traditions and the achievements of this field. He is less likely to follow the old groove than the man experienced in the field, for he has a fresh and unhampered outlook on the problem. Another important advantage lies in the fact that he brings to the field a knowledge and outlook that the others in that field do not have. This enables him to form novel and unusual combinations which would be considered folly by the experienced men even if merely suggested as a possibility. The ignorance of the failure of others is also in his favor for he is not hesitant and doubtful. He attacks his problem with confidence, courage, and great energy. For these reasons an electrical engineer never connected the idea of sound transmission with an electromagnet. The electrical engineer was immersed too much in his own field to see beyond it or combine it with facts from other fields. The southern planters cleaned their cotton for many years by the manual labor of slaves. They took it for granted that this was the only way it could be done, until Whitney came from New England where machines were replacing human labor and he showed them how it could be done. The carriage makers could not possibly visualize any other motive power except horses for their carriages. In the same way, we often find the experienced men in their respective fields to be conservative and with limited vision. They accept what they find and seldom question authority. For these reasons the amateur or the so-called outsider very often makes important inventions and discoveries.

We have seen in Chapter III that our large industrial organizations have not produced the majority of our epoch-making inventions. The telegraph companies, for instance, did not invent the telephone. The gas companies did not invent the electric light. The horse-car railways did not invent the electric railway. In each case a man not familiar with the particular industry made the invention which ultimately displaced or improved the old industry. These men were innovators, not bound by any precedent or prejudice and, therefore, had vision to do what the men in the industry could not even imagine as a possibility. We must remember, of course, that corporations have a great deal of money invested in their equipment and business and it is, therefore, to be expected that they would use their equipment and machinery as long as possible in order to obtain the maximum profits. No industry would be willing to scrap millions of dollars worth of machinery in favor of a new invention if they could prevent it. The gas companies would naturally want to use their gas producers and costly piping systems as long as possible instead of adopting something entirely different as the electric light. The inventor employed by such corporations naturally becomes conservative and bound, more or less, by the policy of his company so that most of his inventions will aim at improving the existing equipment rather than making new or radical departures which would be too expensive to adopt.

Another reason for the lack of correlation of the basic inventions with the occupation of their inventors is due to the fact that the basic inventions are so entirely different from their most closely related fields that there is no more reason for workers in these fields to invent than for inventors not in the field. Basic inventions also create new industries and by their very nature are far removed from any known industry. The basic inventor is thus an "outsider" because there are as yet no "insiders" in the new industry.

We find that it is primarily for economic reasons that inventors usually confine their inventions to their specific occupation. Their job is to improve what is already being used and consumed. Competition and the pressure of the public of course bring about many improvements but these are usually confined to their specific line of work. Table 6 gives a summary of the replies of 452 inventors in response to the question "Are all your inventions confined to your line of work?"

TABLE 6

THE RELATION OF THE TYPE OF INVENTIONS TO OCCUPATION OF INVENTORS

Answer	No. of Inventors	Per cent
All inventions confined to occupation	225	49.8
Not all inventions confined to occupation	227	50.2
Total	452	100.0

We see that nearly half of the inventors confine themselves strictly to their line of work. Most inventions today are improvement inventions caused by strenuous competition and economic pressure. The manufacturer today seeks to improve his product and to produce it at lower costs by mass production. Our technical knowledge has increased by such great strides that it takes many years of study and training to understand the technology already developed. Consequently we find that most inventions today are produced by men who are actively engaged in the fields to which their inventions relate. We are also having an increasing number of hired inventors who are employed to invent in a specified field. Naturally the inventions of such men would be entirely restricted to a single field. As time goes on and technical progress increases inventors will probably be forced to specialize even to a greater extent in their specific fields than they are doing today.

Conditions today are different than they were in the days when the great epoch-making industrial inventions, such as those mentioned in the beginning of the chapter, were being made in quick succession. Great industries have been developed upon these inventions employing millions of workers and technically-trained men. The majority of inventors today come from the industries. This is shown in Table 7 which gives the occupation of the 710 inventors who gave the data for this study.

TABLE 7
OCCUPATION OF 710 INVENTORS

	Number	Per cent
Engineers	425	59.8
Executives	169	23.8
Mechanics	38	5.4
Professional inventors	14	2.0
Patent lawyers	12	1.7
Merchants	5	0.7
Farmers	5	0.7
Miscellaneous	42	5.9
Total	710	100.0

Considerably more than half of these inventors are employed in the engineering fields. This group includes the various engineering occupations in the mechanical, electrical and chemical fields in the industries. We would naturally expect the men in these occupations to constitute the greater part of the inventors because they come into intimate contact with all the technical phases of the industries and are the most likely ones to be called on for solving problems which arise and meeting new needs or difficulties.

The executives in Table 7 consist largely of the presidents and vice-presidents of the manufacturing companies. It is extremely interesting to note that this group amounts to almost one-quarter of the entire number of inventors. These men are at the helm of their organizations and they are usually the most active and enterprising men in the organization, so that we would expect them to do a great deal of inventing. Many of these men actually made the initial inventions on which their company exists and operates. It is also highly probable that many of these executives were originally engineers who were advanced to executive positions. Executives are also in a position to receive suggestions and hints from their employees and salesmen, who very often give them ideas for new inventions. We must also remember that group invention is becoming a common thing in the industries and very often the executives are credited with an invention which has been actually worked out by a large number of men employed by the organization. The group designated executives also includes general managers, directors of research and superintendents who total to 21.9 per cent of the executives. The remarks made in regard to the presidents also apply with equal force to them.

It is also interesting to note that there are comparatively few mechanics (only 5.4 per cent) in this group of inventors. This does not necessarily mean that the extremely active inventors today are not recruited from this class of workers. In order to be an inventor it is, of course, not necessary to be a practical mechanic. The mechanical details of an invention can be worked out by an engineer, machine designer or draughtsman and after the specifications are developed in detail the parts can be readily made by any mechanic or machinist. However, we must remember that when a mechanic is prolific in inventing he will most likely advance to an executive position. It is probably for this reason that the percentage of mechanics is low, as many of them are found in the group of executives. A mechanic who is a prolific inventor is also apt to call himself an engineer.

The patent lawyers present an interesting question whether contact with inventions leads to inventing, as they come into intimate contact with inventions and their inventors. We should, therefore, expect many of them to invent as a consequence. This is actually confirmed by Table 8 which gives a summary of the replies of 176 patent attorneys to the question whether they patented any of their inventions.

TABLE 8

INVENTIONS MADE BY PATENT ATTORNEYS

	Number	Per cent
Attorneys who made inventions	104	63.4
Attorneys who made no inventions	60	36.6
No answer	12	—
Total	176	100.0

We find that 63.4 per cent of the patent attorneys have made and patented their own inventions. Apparently contact with inventions stimulates invention. Many patent attorneys often invent for their clients in order to help them to avoid the infringement of outstanding patents. Improvements also often suggest themselves when they are working on their clients' inventions. These inventions are usually patented by the attorneys who assign them to their clients.

CHAPTER X

THE MOTIVES OF INVENTORS

SEVERAL pages could be easily filled with a list of human cravings and strivings without making the list exhaustive. These cravings constitute the basis of our motives and incentives which are largely the basis of human behavior. Motives are the mainspring of action. They are the cause of the great persistence and patience of the inventor in making his inventions. All motives can ultimately be reduced to the fundamental human desires such as food, sex, shelter and survival. In a complex civilization these primitive drives to action are still potent and active not only in their original forms but also in many diversified sublimated forms.

As stated by Hollingworth: "Motives are not vaporous entities, hovering tenuously about the individual. They are concrete, particular events in nature. They are actual present stimuli which lead so directly to other events that their nature is often easily mystified. Chiefly, in human life, motives are annoyances. They are occurring patterns or complexes, of sensory, affective and relational items. They often involve the general state of the organism as part of a total situation which includes other objects or events. Typically, motives are felt patterns of distress, want, craving, annoyance. In daily life, instead of describing them, we apply to them the names of situations in which they originate or of the results to which they lead.

"To satisfy such a persistent stimulus or motive is to remove it or change it for less annoying stimuli. Often motives may be annulled by any of a variety of consequents. Such consequents, however, are not motives. They are means or instruments for alleviating motives.

Motives are impulsive; they urgently lead to responses. This fact gives mental activities their drive and constitutes their energy." [1]

One of the great differences between human and animal behavior is that human behavior is often caused by remote and obscure motives which cannot be satisfied by a single direct act as in satisfying the simple organic urges. A long series of preliminary acts extending over a long period of time may often be necessary. This is well illustrated by the inventor who goes through a long series of involved and complicated acts in making an invention.

What are the motives which urge the inventor to invent? Money has often been mentioned as the outstanding objective. The perception of a need and the joy of inventing are also mentioned frequently. In order to throw light on this question, the inventors of this study were asked "What motives or incentives cause you to invent?" Table 9 gives a summary of the frequencies of the replies.

TABLE 9

FREQUENCY OF MOTIVES OR INCENTIVES MENTIONED BY 710 INVENTORS

Motive	Frequency
Love of inventing	193
Desire to improve	189
Financial gain	167
Necessity or need	118
Desire to achieve	73
Part of work	59
Prestige	27
Altruistic reasons	22
Laziness	6
No answers	33

An inspection of Table 9 shows that the love of inventing is the motive most frequently mentioned. The sheer joy of inventing, resulting from an irrepressible urge to invent has been felt as the greatest urge by the inven-

[1] H. L. Hollingworth, Psychology, its facts and principles, New York, Appleton, 1928, 317.

tors of this study. The pleasure resulting from manipulation and experimentation, the satisfaction of solving problems and the desire to create, were considered sufficient in themselves as objectives by the inventors. As stated by Taussig: "One thing stands out conspicuously: the race of contrivers and inventors does obey an inborn and irresistible impulse. Schemes and experiments begin in childhood, and persist so long as life and strength hold. It matters not whether a fortune is made or pecuniary distress is chronic: there is increasing interest in new dodges, unceasing trial of new devices.

"Cartwright was in difficulties almost all his life: yet he never relaxed his interest in any and every sort of mechanical devices. Edison made fortunes and lost them and made them again; but throughout he remained the same amazing and persistent contriver. And it would seem that no satisfaction from pecuniary success or worldly recognition equals the absorbed interest of trial, experiment, novel problems, happy solutions.

"Not only is the instinct imperious; it is generic. We are misled by the fact that the names of most inventors are associated with one device, at most two: Watt with the steam-engine, Cartwright with the power-loom and the combining machine, Fulton with the steamboat, Howe with the sewing-machine, Ericsson with the screw propeller and the monitor, Bell with the telephone, Edison with the incandescent light and the moving picture. Their biographies show that they were constantly experimenting on all sorts of schemes, promising and unpromising; sometimes with money-making intent, sometimes in the spirit of scientific research, and sometimes merely in sport. Werner Siemens, one of the few who combined a strictly scientific temper with the genius for contrivance, began with the telegraph, proceeded to the metallurgy of iron and copper, closed with devotion to the field of pure science. Cartwright turned his daring and original mind to a host of contrivances. Fulton gave years to canals and to submarine boats before he turned to steamboats, and was ready with a plan for an armored man-o'war when the commercial steamboat had been only half perfected. Ericsson was intent on a dozen devices, among which the caloric (hot-air) engine was conspicuous." [2]

These remarks apply not only to the prominent inventors of the past, but as the results of this study show, they apply with equal force to the present-day active inventor. It is rare that inventors make a single invention. They are recidivists, constantly planning and designing new inventions. No sooner is one invention completed than others are planned forthwith.

The desire to improve existing devices comes a very close second to the love of inventing, being very closely related to the love of inventing as one of its phases. The objective of most inventors today is to make things better, cheaper, and more efficiently. The desire to change things and to improve them is not only common to the inventor but also to the manufacturer. This is largely due to increased competition and to our population which is educated to enjoy the latest luxuries.

Financial gain is the third most frequently mentioned motive of the inventors. A great deal has been written on money as the incentive to invention. Many people believe that it is the uppermost and most important urge to invent. We find, however, that this is not the case with the inventors of this study. This is extremely interesting because we must remember that we are dealing with a very active group of inventors. It is difficult, of course, to evaluate the frankness with which these answers were made. Assurance was given in the letter accompanying the questionnaire that the replies would be kept confidential and used for statistical purposes. Very little evidence was found in the replies to indicate any lack of sincerity.

We must bear in mind that the mere love of inventing would in itself often be insufficient to be an incentive to

[2] F. W. Taussig, Inventors and money-makers, New York, Macmillan, 1915, 21-23.

invention. Before any invention is perfected and marketed a great deal of money must be spent in developing and perfecting the original mental conception. The inventor either must spend his own money or interest business men in his invention. In either case, unless there was a prospect of gain, the chances are that no money would be spent in developing the invention to a practical basis. We must agree with Taussig that "the direction in which the contriver turns his bent is immensely affected by the prospect of gain for himself. Now, gain and profit come from supplying people with what they want; and the influence of individual interest on the direction of inventor's activity turns it toward the promotion of the general welfare." [3]

"The most that can be laid down, as the outcome of the present discussion, is that inventors on the whole need the spur of profits as much as the others whose creative and guiding activity is indispensable for human progress." [4]

Professor Taussig, like others, refers to the instinct of contrivance. In recent years, however, the term "instinct" has come into disrepute in these discussions not so much because it is not a useful term but because it was used as a means to hide our ignorance of the ulterior problems. As Hollingworth has stated: "Of one thing we can be reasonably certain. This is that most of the 'instincts' attributed to man are instead early acquired and well-nigh universally established habits. Thus it is often said that men instinctively seize, collect, hoard, and struggle to retain whatever they get their hands upon. This 'collecting instinct,' 'native acquisitiveness,' 'property sense,' 'selfishness,' and so on is then cited as an inherited propensity upon which many social institutions are based.

---

[3] F. W. Taussig, Inventors and money-makers, New York, Macmillan, 1915, 50.

[4] Ibid., 53.

"While definite proof is lacking on one side as well as on the other, it seems reasonably clear that such human activities are not determined by the structure of the human creature. They are most of all dependent upon the character of the world into which he is born. Suppose, for example, that instead of this world being characterized by a dearth of commodities, it were filled with everything that could be used or desired.

"The so-called human instincts, at least, are in the main only learned techniques for the alleviation of such wants. They are habit devices for the elimination of annoyances, the satisfaction of cravings, in a world chiefly characterized by poverty of commodities. Fighting, hunting, courting, gregariousness, curiosity, and all the other honored 'human instincts' seem similarly accountable." [5]

And yet, although the inventor may not be driven by the so-called instinct of contrivance in the psychological or biological sense, there is no question that he is impelled by a powerful drive to contrive, which for the purpose of the social and economic student, acts like an instinct. Inventors, like other creative workers experience an irrepressible and deep-seated urge to create at an early age. The satisfaction of this urge is a source of deep gratification and pleasure. This desire for creative expression coupled with the incentive of gain has given us some of our greatest inventions.

Yet, inventors, having the same needs and wants as their fellow beings, and living in an industrial age dominated by money standards, cannot ignore the necessity of earning money, even though they may feel that the primary incentive to invent is the mere love of inventing. The data relating to the livelihood of inventors throw an interesting light on this question. The following Table gives the results of the replies to the question "Do you earn your livelihood by inventing?"

---

[5] H. L. Hollingworth, Psychology, its facts and principles, New York, Appleton, 1928, 336.

TABLE 10
LIVELIHOOD OF INVENTORS

	Number	Per cent
Earn livelihood by inventing	265	38.2
Do not earn livelihood by inventing	271	39.1
Partially	158	22.7
No answer	16	
Total	710	100.0

Table 10 shows that the prospect of financial gain is, after all, an important factor in inventing, especially when 38 per cent of the inventors earn their livelihood thereby.

Practically all of the inventors of this study were also found to be married, as shown in Table 11 giving the marital status of the inventors.

TABLE 11
MARITAL STATUS OF 710 INVENTORS

Married	643
Not married	32
Widower	9
Divorced	2
No answer	24
Total	710

The extremely high proportion of married inventors as indicated in Table 11 would tend to make even more clear the importance of the monetary reward to the inventor as the marital status definitely increases his economic needs.

In this connection it is interesting to quote from Hart: "A group of graduate students at Bryn Mawr made a study of 171 men who had made significant contributions to mechanical invention. The hope of making money from the invention was noted only five times in the material located relative to these inventors, while the joy of manipulating materials, of experimentation and exploration, appeared in connection with 66 different inventors. Next most important in the apparent motivation of inventors is the perception of a need to be met—a problem to be solved. Not a reward to be won at the end of the struggle, but the pleasure of the inventive process, the zest of pitting one's power against a puzzling obstacle, the fun of using one's mental and mechanical abilities—in a word the joy of functioning—is the driving power that keeps the typical inventor going." [6]

The inventors mentioned in Hart's study were taken from Kaempfert's "A Popular History of American Invention." Most of these inventors were active fifty or more years ago, so that it was not possible to obtain data from the men themselves, as in the present inquiry. The results of Hart's study are more unqualified in finding the main motive of inventors to be the joy of exploration and manipulation. This is probably due to the fact that the data were obtained from biographical material of a popular kind, which would probably dramatize and glorify the inventors. The results cannot be considered very trustworthy or significant.

Returning to Table 9 we find that necessity, need, or an obstacle are frequently mentioned as an incentive by the inventors of this study. As we have seen in Chapter VI, the necessity or need really initiates the entire inventive process and it is, therefore, of the highest importance to the inventor as an incentive, particularly as a proximate cause. We cannot, after all, select any one motive as being more important than another. The motives of inventors as well as non-inventors are highly complex systems made up of many forces pulling in different directions. As Professor Taussig says: "The case, in truth, is almost invariably one of mixed motives. That very Fulton who bargained so shrewdly in selling his inventions, good and bad, was unquestionably sincere, though doubtless exuberant of emphasis, when he wrote: 'Although the prospect of personal emolument has been some inducement to me, yet I feel infinitely more pleasure in reflecting on the immense advantages that my country will draw from the invention' (of the steamboat). Edison had the same mixed feeling; further complicated by an

[6] H. Hart, Science of social relations, New York, Holt, 1927, 19.

influence which has become of growing strength in modern times, professional pride and professional recognition. It is rare that a man feels a single impulse so strongly that the others are pushed aside and rendered inoperative; and it is rare also that a man in whom one trait is highly developed manifests a similar extreme with any other. Among the instincts which we shall presently have to consider is one quite neglected by the older economists—that of sympathy, devotion, public spirit. Like the rest, it appears with overpowering and far-ranging force in some individuals; in others it seems to be confined strictly to the narrow range of the domestic affections. Just as very few men are both capable business managers and ingenious inventors, so few are at the same time ingenious inventors and exalted altruists." [7]

In the present inquiry many and varied motives were mentioned by the inventors, such as the desire for achievement, altruism, prestige, superiority, fame, praise, recognition, honor, leisure, influence, power, and so forth. They were mentioned with little frequency, however, as compared with the four major motives—love of inventing, desire to improve, financial gain, and necessity or need.

Inventors, after all, are practical men who express their ideas in physical form at the expense of time and money. It is, therefore, only natural that they should not be content with honor or glory alone as a reward. Even though the greatest and immediate reward of the inventor is the sheer joy of the work, inventing is a business undertaken with a hope of profit. The experience of a need or necessity usually initiates the inventive process; in order to bring it to a successful completion the dynamic spur of profit, coupled with joy derived from creating or improving, is essential. From the psychological standpoint, however, it remains true that the love of inventing is the most powerful motive of inventors.

[7] F. W. Taussig, Inventors and money-makers, New York, Macmillan, 1915, 48, 49.

CHAPTER XI

OBSTACLES AND PITFALLS OF INVENTORS *

THE OBSTACLES and pitfalls which confront all inventors are legion. One inventor has humorously said that "every contemplated invention is an obstacle." It seems to be the lot of innovators in all fields to meet with opposition, apathy, and prejudice. The inventors at the beginning of the industrial revolution in England were treated with hostility, unfriendliness and often with actual violence. Their machines were smashed and the inventors were regarded by the ignorant workers as their enemies because they feared that their inventions would cause them to lose their jobs. The inventor today is, of course, treated differently and is recognized more or less as an important cog in the industrial machine, but in spite of his economic importance he is still meeting with a great many obstacles which tend to prevent him from completing his inventions.

The essential difference between the inventor and other creative workers is that the inventor's creation is ultimately put to a commercial test. An invention must be socially useful, it must be practical, it must be easy to manufacture, it must be durable, it must withstand abuse and constant usage, it must make profits for the manufacturer. No wonder the inventor meets with difficulties. From the first mental conception of his invention to its final manufacture and commercialization he must always take account of economic facts. At no time can he avoid meeting the test of practicability. These and other obstacles to be overcome by the inventor can be divided broadly as relating to the art of inventing itself, the

* Reprinted with changes from the Journal of the Patent Office Society. By Joseph Rossman, May, 1930.

financing, the manufacturing, and the marketing of the invention.

Before going very far the inventor must, of course, invent. This means that he must follow all the actual and psychological steps outlined in Chapters V and VI. He may, of course, meet with obstacles at any point in the inventive process. He may lack ability, he may have insufficient knowledge, he may be easily discouraged, he may not be sufficiently thorough, or he may be unable to concentrate on his work. These are, of course, obstacles which are found in himself and which he himself must overcome.

The greatest obstacles an inventor meets, however, are found in his external environment. He must take into account the economic conditions, the prejudices of people, the dishonesty of some promoters, the problems of manufacturing and selling his invention.

The framers of our Constitution recognized the great importance of invention in the progress of the country and, therefore, specifically provided for the reward of the inventor in order to encourage invention. As a result we have our present patent system. A patent today, however, is seldom a real reward to the inventor, on account of the many defects in the patent system. Even if the patent were fool-proof legally, the inventor would have to combat with many obstacles and avoid innumerable pitfalls. The Government has taken no direct interest in the welfare of the inventor except in granting him a patent and the value of this patent depends entirely on the skill and ability of his patent attorney and not on the merits of his invention. The many conditions adverse to the inventor which prevail today have, therefore, forced most inventors to enter the employ of large organizations in order to live. The simplest inventions require the expenditure of thousands of dollars, the services of many experts and specialists before the invention is actually marketed. Very few inventors can meet such rigorous requirements and their only recourse is either to interest some promoters or to drop their brain-child, for the Government is utterly indifferent and has no facilities to give him expert advice or assistance. As one inventor has said, "We are nothing but intellectual serfs."

In order to determine the greatest obstacles met in inventing, the inventors of this study were asked to enumerate them. Table 12 gives a summary of the results.

TABLE 12

OBSTACLES MENTIONED BY 710 INVENTORS

Obstacle	Number
Lack of capital	136
Lack of knowledge	93
Prejudice	69
Legal difficulties	55
Marketing	54
Anticipation by others	39
Lack of time	38
Lack of facilities	23
No obstacles	96

We could probably guess that lack of capital is the inventor's greatest obstacle. This is an obstacle in nearly all fields of human endeavor. The need of money is, of course, felt most acutely by the individual inventor. The group inventor in the employ of a large company seldom faces this problem in regard to his invention as it is taken care of by his company. In either case before the public can benefit from any invention three important steps are necessary—the creation of the invention, capitalization, and commercialization. Unfortunately creative ability does not often run with business ability. The inventor who attempts to capitalize and finance his invention is very often in a strange and unfamiliar field. He does not know how to raise money or how to organize his efforts and those of others in the most efficient manner. Naturally, there are many heavy losses incurred.

According to Vaughn, who has made a study of the economic aspects of our patent system: "Modern methods of manufacturing and marketing a new product, and especially a complicated one, demand an initial outlay of large proportions. Machinery for making the invention must be perfected and its introduction to the public requires salesmen and advertising. Moreover, those who introduce patented machinery are compelled by the very haste of its evolution, continually to modify it. It costs $200,000 to make the tools and machines that are necessary to put a typewriter on the market, at a salable price, even before any advertising is done. Dr. Baekeland said that he has been personally identified with enterprises which could only begin to work an invention after investing to the extent of $1,200,000 for plans alone. The alliance between the inventor and the capitalist is more important now than formerly because of the increasing complexity and cost of modern devices. The capitalist furnishes the power of waiting, an indispensable function in the development of an invention. One inventor has expressed the opinion that few patents of merit have ever been brought to a marketable condition, on an average, in less than ten years. In fact, inventors often lose possible profits because they are not willing to wait for slow returns." [1]

Another writer states: "A most important phase of invention as contrasted with what is typical of scientific discovery is the capital necessary to be expended during the period of perfecting the invention and introducing it to make it commercially acceptable. For the first named activity alone, Paige, an inventor of a typesetting machine in which Mark Twain became interested, spent $1,300,000. Many thousands of dollars, labor and time were expended in bringing to operative condition the linotype and monotype inventions, while Curtis' steam turbine required several millions of dollars before it was ready for introduction. This expenditure, in various degrees, is an inherent feature in almost all inventions, and becomes an overhead and a liability on the invention,

[1] F. L. Vaughn, Economics of our patent system, New York, Macmillan, 1925, 216-217.

as competitors are free of it, unless it is protected by patent grant." [2]

The inventors also state that lack of knowledge is a great obstacle. Very often the solution of a problem is made impossible because the inventor fails to have some pertinent information at his command. This may be due to his lack of training or to his failure to make a complete search of the technical literature bearing on his problem. Lack of knowledge may also include the ignorance of the fundamental laws of physics and chemistry, the basic engineering principles of his own field or a knowledge of what has been done before him. The inventor may also fail to investigate all the economic aspects of his invention such as the possible demand for his product, the cost of manufacturing and marketing, the competitors in the field, the possibility of infringing patents owned by other concerns, and the patent situation in general in regard to his own invention. The failure of knowing all the details of these factors may lead to many serious difficulties.

Chas. C. Worthington, a prolific inventor, has stated in this connection in a personal letter: "The time has come when the Government should make it possible for any citizen having discovered something he wished to patent, to present his discovery to a competent Board appointed especially to pass upon the merits of the invention in such a case and to advise whether it is worth following up or should be abandoned. The opinion of this Board would be looked upon, in the majority of cases as conclusive. This arrangement would enable the impecunious inventor to have an equal chance with the rich, which he does not now possess, on account of the expense of the course he now has to follow.

"The men composing these Boards should be authorized to secure in special cases, the aid of Experts known to be competent authorities on the subjects in hand.

"The most important feature of such a plan would be

[2] W. I. Wyman, Patents for scientific discoveries, Journal of the Patent Office Society, 1929, 11, 533-557.

that the vast loss of time and money now wasted by the average inventor, often to the point of ruining him and his family, would be in the main prevented. This annual wastage is a crying evil. It develops unscrupulous attorneys who now entice their ignorant, optimistic clients to go to the expense of a patent application for manifestly worthless contrivances. The Government should not be a party to such subversive schemes. Many people otherwise capable of making valuable discoveries to science or manufacture, are discouraged today from developing and patenting their ideas by the expense and delays attendant upon our Patent Office procedure. This procedure is now too discouraging, expensive and slow to permit the inventive genius of the country to properly develop. The country owes it to its inventors to make their way easier."

The same inventor also stated that "the inventor must not jump at the conclusion that an idea, because his own, must be new. In a vast majority of cases it is old and either worthless, obsolete or public property. Vast sums have been spent and thousands of lives devoted to the more or less secret pursuit of chimerical inventions, that a little investigation in the right direction would have been shown to lead to nothing but pathetic disappointment. All this is due to the mistaken notion that anyone can hit upon something valuable in the way of an innovation, without first becoming fully informed concerning the thing sought to be improved and with the state of the art."

Closely related to the lack of capital is the lack of time and facilities to complete the invention. An inventor harassed by the need of money will naturally not have much time to devote to his experiments and study. He will either spend his time trying to make a living or raising sufficient capital to finance his invention. The inability to obtain materials necessary for making an invention are often very serious obstacles. The search for the proper material may sometimes entail an expensive search and a long series of costly experiments. Unless the inventor can obtain the facilities for experiment he will not progress very far. Even assuming that he has embodied his invention in physical form, many tests and experiments are necessary before the final embodiment of the invention is completed. Invention is largely a matter of opportunity and a man with poor resources is not likely to perfect his inventions.

We have previously noted that all innovators meet with opposition and prejudice even to the point of physical violence. The mass dislikes new things. Most people would rather do things as they have been accustomed to do them. There seems to be something in human nature which resists change. The inventors of our most useful inventions spent many years convincing the public of the usefulness and utility of their devices. They met with apathy, indifference and prejudice everywhere.

Rear Admiral Fiske, a well-known inventor, has said, "Many an inventor has endured a purgatory while trying to get a hearing for his invention, and yet been wholly forgotten when it was finally adopted."

Business men, even today, are slow in accepting new inventions. There may be many inventors who find no obstacles in making their inventions but they encounter obstacles in placing them. The human race has an enormous inertia and hates to be deviated from its usual course by any new schemes or methods. Any one who attempts to invent against custom and habit is bound to have a difficult time. Thousands of inventions have waited for many years before their merits were appreciated. The Patent Office records are full of the buried hopes of unknown inventors. Initiative and courage are just as important in impressing ideas upon others as they have always been in impressing our control on the physical world.

The marketing of an invention is an art in itself. First of all, it requires a great expenditure of money. If the product is entirely new a great deal of advertising may be necessary. Another difficulty is to properly estimate the market demand. Will this be sufficient to warrant profitable production, and how long will it take to reach that point? Also, of course, what expenditure of money will be required to carry the article through to a self-sustaining basis? The mechanical difficulties are frequently the least, provided a man is properly trained and equipped for his work. The manufacturing difficulties must be thoroughly analyzed and studied so that the invention can be produced cheaply and in the best possible commercial form.

The particular group of people for whom the invention is intended must be approached personally in some way. The merits of the invention must be made obvious. The resistance to its adoption must be overcome. In these days of specialization and intricacy of commercial methods it is almost folly for the inventor to attempt this difficult step without the aid of men who know this business thoroughly. The prime work of the inventor is to create his invention. Of course, under the economic conditions today he must also interest business men in his new invention and convince them of its merits. Business men are in most cases best fitted to undertake the difficult task of marketing the invention. According to Taussig, "The alliance of the inventor with the business man in command of capital is probably more important now than in older days, because of the increasing complexity and cost of modern devices." [3]

There are many legal obstacles which most inventors encounter sooner or later. One inventor of this study stated that "The greatest obstacle and pitfall to the American inventor is the American patent law itself." The very first obstacle is the intricate matter of obtaining a patent. Our patent law has become so complicated that one judge has called it the metaphysics of the law. A knowledge of the fundamentals of patent law is highly

[3] F. W. Taussig, Inventors and money-makers, New York, Macmillan, 1915, 41.

essential to all inventors. Actually, we find that very few inventors are versed in the legal aspect of patent matters. As a result they must rely on their patent attorneys about whom more will be said later. A knowledge of a few elementary principles of patent law might have saved many inventors bitter disappointments and the losses of their due reward.

Patents were originally intended to be the reward of the inventor. It is highly questionable whether this is actually the case today. One inventor has even gone so far as to state that "patents are a snare and an abomination." It is generally admitted that our patent system has many defects which should be remedied. F. L. Vaughn in his book the "Economics of Our Patent System" concludes that our patent laws today are inadequate and fail to protect or reward the inventor. He finds that the patent laws are used by many wealthy corporations in order to create monopolies and destroy competition.

According to Vaughn: "The theory of the patent system, more than a century ago, was that the inventor himself would make and sell his invention. It was a time of relatively simple devices, the production and sale of which required no great outlay of capital. Large scale production and a national market, however, make this theory inapplicable today." [4]

Our patent laws today are consequently full of many defects and evils which operate to the detriment of the inventor as well as the public. The fundamental idea underlying the patent system is, however, logical and sound. We must modify our patent laws and legal procedure relating to all aspects of patents so that invention will be encouraged to the fullest extent.

Upon obtaining his first patent, the inventor may be thrilled with the words "exclusive right to make, use and vend the invention" but he will soon find out that his patent is subject to all prior rights and that it merely

[4] F. L. Vaughn, Economics of our patent system, New York, Macmillan, 1925, 216.

gives him the use of the Federal courts to prevent others from making, using or selling his invention as defined by the claims and provided he has disclosed fully some new and useful invention. The inventor always had the right to make, use and vend his invention but it is up to him to exclude others from so doing after he gets his patent. The patentee, that is, the one who is granted the patent, receives nothing from the law which he did not have before, and the only effect of his patent is to restrain others from manufacturing, using or selling that which he has invented. The inventor, therefore, especially if he has a valuable patent will soon find himself suing his infringers. The Government merely gives him the right to sue, but he himself must be the one to enforce his rights and he must go in a Federal court of equity to enforce them.

The world has not yet thoroughly learned that an invention is property in the sense of real estate, and therefore it does not hesitate to appropriate it if it can do so with impunity. "Any inventor may, justly or unjustly, be forced into litigation, and if he lacks the means to make a proper defense, the property rights of the patent and the expense of discovering and developing the invention are a total loss. The inventor's meritorious property is frequently as effectively confiscated as if there were no law protecting it. Eighty-five per cent of the people of the United States are generally classed as poor, and this applies disproportionately to inventors at the critical stage, for the evident reason that the time and money spent in discovering and developing an inventive idea cannot also be directed toward productive income. Not one in a thousand inventors is financially able to adequately defend his just rights against patent pirates or against individuals or corporations with large financial resources, who, in good or bad faith, start litigation or commit infringement.

"The mere filing of a lawsuit against a patent usually prevents temporarily, if not permanently, further exploitation of the invention, injures or ruins the business;

causes royalties to be cut off; the inventor is usually rendered financially helpless to properly defend the patent and his outlook on life is temporarily depressed; and, facing the prospect of long drawn-out, expensive litigation in trial and appellate courts before judges who likely have little or no proper understanding of the technical details of the art involved, his respect for the law is shattered. The dissipated time and energy of both litigants in such an idiotic procedure represents a loss to them and to the State. The law, instead of being an instrument of justice, is made the tool for the most outrageous injustice. A law to be respected must be respectable and be respectably administered. The law, pertaining to present patent litigation is neither respectable nor is it respectably administered, assuming, and rightly so, with relatively few exceptions, that the judges are intelligent, honest, and well informed in the law." [5]

As one inventor of this study has said, "if an inventor happens to develop something worth while and obtains a patent he is simply getting a ticket for the most exciting joy ride any one can get in this nation." According to Vaughn: "The expense of defending one's patents frequently equals or exceeds the revenue derived from them. About $1,000,000 was spent to prevent the infringement of the Edison incandescent lamp. The president of Thomas A. Edison, Inc., once stated that Edison had spent more money in obtaining patents, litigating them, and preventing infringements of them than he had received from his patents as such." [6]

Edison, himself, has recently said in an interview reported in the *Saturday Evening Post*, September 27, 1930: "I have made very little profit from my inventions. In my lifetime I have taken out 1180 patents, up to date. Counting the expense of experimenting and fighting for

[5] W. Greenawalt and K. W. Greenawalt, A plea for a U. S. Court of Patent Appeals, Mining and Metallurgy, 1930, 11, 85-90.

[6] F. L. Vaughn, Economics of our patent system, New York, Macmillan, 1925, 181.

my claims in court, these patents have cost me more than they have returned me in royalties. I have made money through the introduction and sale of my products as a manufacturer, not as an inventor.

"We have a miserable system in the United States for protecting inventions from infringement. I have known of several inventors who were poor. Their ideas would have made them millionaires, but they were kept poor by the pirates who were allowed through our very faulty system of protection to usurp their rights. The usurpation is particularly apt to obtain in the case of some great epoch making patent."

Dr. Reginald Fessenden, an inventor of great importance, has said in this connection: "Nor am I interested in any way financially, for up to date I have yet to receive the first penny for any of my patents. Once I was urged to take up the matter of my wireless telephone patents, as the company which had them had made a profit of over five hundred thousand dollars in one year and was in addition drawing large royalties from the Marconi company for the wireless telegraph applications. The verdict was for four hundred and six thousand dollars and forty-five per cent of the stock, but the company had anticipated the decision and went into a receivership before it was given, the directors sold themselves the patents, and later disposed of them for five million dollars; so, as the legal expenses had been heavy I decided not to bother about such matters until the laws were amended to give inventors better protection; and have obtained the money necessary for developing my inventions by work along other lines." [7]

Another serious obstacle to inventors is the delay in obtaining patents. The Patent Office is literally swamped with thousands of applications awaiting to be acted on. Congress has not provided an adequate personnel and has made little or no efforts to retain the examiners who leave the Patent Office for more

[7] R. A. Fessenden, The deluged civilization, Boston, T. J. Print, 1923, 127.

lucrative positions in the industries. The quality of the work performed by the Patent Office is thus seriously impaired by the constant stream of experienced examiners leaving the office. Claims and patents are allowed which should never issue on account of poor searches by inexperienced examiners. These invalid patents harm not only the inventor, but also the public for they may be the basis of expensive litigation costing thousands of dollars.

Another obstacle to the inventor in the American patent law is the interference procedure and its complicated mechanism relating to the so-called proof of priority. For example, an inventor relates that he applied for a patent and then disclosed his invention to a large corporation which is controlling a certain industry. The corporation, being under unscrupulous management and not wishing to buy the invention from the inventor, then instructed one of its engineers to design a device similar to the one made by the inventor for which he filed an application. The two applications went into interference and the unscrupulous corporation found some ways and means to prove that they conceived the idea before the inventor who offered his invention to them.

In case a corporation cannot prove priority, they can very easily prevent the issuance of the patent to the inventor for as long as ten years by filing one appeal after another with the result that the poor inventor, having exhausted all his means on his invention is compelled to sell it to the corporation at their own stipulated price.

However, most of the interferences instituted in the Patent Office are entirely honest and legitimate and are caused by the process of multiple invention, as we have seen in Chapter VIII. But even under these circumstances they are extremely expensive and entail a loss of much time and effort.

Another legal obstacle to the inventor is the difficulty caused by contracts which are usually signed between an employer and the employee at the inception of employment in which the employee agrees to assign all the inventions to his employer. Many inventors of this study complained about such agreements forced upon them, as it tends to deaden incentive and kills all inventive initiative, because they receive no actual remuneration for their inventions beyond their regular salary.

It is interesting to note there were some inventors who stated that they met with no obstacles. The majority of these inventors were either executives or were employed to invent by large companies. In such a situation we would expect them not to meet any obstacles chiefly because they were not concerned with the financing and marketing of their inventions after their inventions were completed.

The inventors of this study were also asked to state what pitfalls an inventor should avoid in making his inventions. Some very interesting remarks were made on this subject. The replies are summarized in Table 13.

TABLE 13
PITFALLS MENTIONED BY 710 INVENTORS

Pitfall	Number
Impracticability	166
Overconfidence	120
Lack of knowledge	112
Patent attorneys	72
Lack of thoroughness	46
Dishonest promoters	43
Discouragement	30
Hope of riches	28
Disclosure to others	23

The inventors stressed as the greatest pitfall the danger of making impractical inventions. The inventor should make sure that there is a real need for the invention, that it is useful, that there is a commercial demand for it, and that it has a market. The failure to meet these tests is certain to bring difficulties to any inventor, no matter how meritorious he may think his invention is. We have already quoted Edison in this connection who said "If it can be done, is it worth doing?" In other words, is it a practical invention which will warrant the investment of capital so as to make profits?

The first essential requisite for any invention is that it must tend to satisfy some real basic human need. The inventor must have something which the people want. It is also important for an inventor who has limited resources not to attempt the commercialization of inventions which require fortunes to be spent before they are launched. Many successful inventors are inclined to pass up ideas which embody devices or equipment running into large sums of money, both in research and development work and also in the cost of the finished article itself. They soon become cumbersome and unwieldy and they require a great deal of capital to exploit. The simple inventions, easy to manufacture and having broad markets appealing to the masses have been the most successful money makers in the past. The manufacturer today is usually interested in something which he can make with his present machinery so that no great expenses will be incurred in developing new machinery.

A great many inventors commit the serious mistake of submitting their crude and incompletely worked out inventions to prospective purchasers. An invention in crude and incomplete form is at best only an idea which requires further design and experimentation in order to determine its value. Manufacturers will naturally hesitate a great deal before investing in a speculative venture depending on a mechanical solution which is not a finished product and which may require much research work for its perfection.

Common sense should dictate to the inventor the hopelessness of attempting the impossible such as perpetual motion. It is astonishing to find the large number of inventors who have in the past centuries attempted to devise perpetual motion devices. The failure of others has meant nothing to them but they went on fully confident of their success. The extent of the perpetual motion activity in the past has been described in detail in a very fascinating book by Dircks entitled "Perpetuum Mobile." [8]

The Patent Office has received numerous applications involving perpetual motion and in such cases it sends the inventor the following letter:

> Sir:
>
> Your application * * * filed complete on * * * involves the elements of perpetual motion. As was said in *ex parte* Payne, 1904 C. D. 42:
>
> "Patents are granted because of the contributions which the inventors are supposed to make to the progress of science and the useful arts. When, therefore, an application is made for a patent on an alleged invention based on principles which run counter to such a well organized law as that of the conservation of energy, the Office is justified in holding that the applicant has not complied with the statutory requirement of showing that the invention is 'sufficiently useful and important' (Rev. Stats. Sec. 4893) to warrant the grant of a patent therefor until he has shown that the invention is capable of operation."
>
> If this case were taken up with the examiner for consideration as to its merits, his first action would be a rejection on the ground of inoperativeness for any useful purpose.
>
> The Office hesitates to accept the filing fees from applicants who believe they have discovered perpetual motion and deems it only fair to give such applicants a word of warning that fees paid cannot be recovered after the case has been considered by the examiner. For these reasons it has been thought best to meet the inventor at the threshold of the Office, and give him an opportunity to recover the moneys paid into the Office.[9]

[8] H. Dircks, Perpetuum mobile, London, Spon, 1870.

[9] E. S. Glascock, Manual of patent office procedure, Federalsburg, Md. J. W. Stowell Co., 1929, 141.

Another serious mistake on the part of the inventor is the failure to recognize that existing facilities in the way of tools and equipment cannot be sacrificed for something different merely because it is different, unless the proposed innovation promises adequate gain in quality of product or profit. The scrapping of an elaborate tool equipment is frequently a very serious matter which must be considered in adopting new designs to supersede older ones.

We have noted in Chapter IV that confidence is one of the traits of an inventor. This trait can be carried to an excess and become an actual pitfall to the inventor as the results in Table 13 show. All inventors have the tendency to regard their invention with a great deal of tenderness and affection. In this emotional attitude they may easily fail to apply the necessary rigid logical tests in order to see if the invention is practical. One or more factors are often overlooked or minimized. The inventor cannot afford to overlook any essential item either in completing or marketing his invention or he is bound to meet with failure. He should not allow his enthusiasm, upon the inception of a new idea, to warp or exclude his judgment as to the utility and commercial practicability of his idea.

Lack of knowledge has been stressed by the inventors as a pitfall as well as an obstacle. In these days of complex technical developments it is essential for an inventor to know his field thoroughly or else he will fall into many blunders and mistakes. This is especially true for inventors who make improvement inventions. An insufficient knowledge of the technical and commercial aspects of a given field may lead to absurd and grotesque inventions.

The inventor should work in the field with which he is familiar and, if possible, should be conversant with the history of the art, and particularly of its most recent developments, otherwise he may be wasting his time in inventing something that has been done before, or be misled as to the practicability and feasibility of his invention through his lack of familiarity with the art and do something that is already done as well or better.

It is interesting to note that patent attorneys have been mentioned as a pitfall. We have already noted the criticisms made against our patent system and mentioned some of its defects. The patent attorney is an important cog in the patent system. The legal protection which our inventor obtains depends entirely on the ability and thoroughness of his patent attorney. The claims constitute the essential part of a patent as they define in extremely technical language the protection granted to the inventor. It is upon these claims that most patent suits and legal proceedings are based. A patent stands or falls on its claims. It is the duty of a good patent attorney to write claims which adequately define the invention and to have the Patent Office allow such claims. An inventor, unless he is intimately acquainted with patent law and procedure, should not attempt to obtain his own patent for he will invariably get into serious difficulties.

The Patent Office has said in this connection that "the preparation of an application is a highly complex proceeding and generally can not be conducted properly except by an attorney trained in this specialized practice. The inventor, therefore, is advised to employ a competent patent attorney who is registered, as without skillful preparation of the specification and claims a patent grant is of doubtful value." [10]

Shoddy patent attorneys should be avoided, especially the kind that guarantees a patent at an attractive price. Patents obtained by such attorneys are often worthless causing the inventor to lose the legal rights to which he is entitled. Quoting Vaughn: "Defective and therefore invalid patents may arise from poor soliciting. It may result in vague and inadequate patents, and therefore poor protection to the inventor. A patent lawyer needs accurate and comprehensive knowledge in order to serve

[10] General information concerning patents, Washington, D. C., U.S. Gov't Printing Office, 1927, 2.

his client and strengthen the legal position of patents. A patent lawyer who knows nothing of technical matters, as is true of many of them, may take out patents which are broader or narrower than the applicant expects and deserves. A patent attorney should possess the two cardinal qualities of ability and honesty. He should advise the inventor not only as to the patentability of the invention, but also as to its probable commercial value. The relationship between them is necessarily one of trust and confidence. The inventor, ignorant of patent law and procedure, must rely upon the ability and integrity of the attorney. It is important not to obtain a patent for its own sake, but to produce one which will secure real protection." [11]

We have already shown that a large number of multiple inventions are made each year which involve many inventors in costly and expensive legal interference proceedings. There is, however, a still larger number of cases of re-invention each year which means that the inventions have been anticipated by others. The data in Table 14 bring out very forcibly the large number of patent applications refused each year by the Patent Office.

TABLE 14

NUMBER OF U. S. PATENT APPLICATIONS AND PATENTS

Year	Applications Filed	Patents Granted	Per cent Refused
1919	80,400	38,598	52.0
1920	86,815	39,882	54.2
1921	93,328	41,401	55.7
1922	88,930	40,297	54.6
1923	79,058	40,787	48.4
1924	80,756	45,500	43.6
1925	84,525	49,540	41.4
1926	86,028	47,627	43.7
1927	92,018	44,444	51.7
1928	92,598	45,899	50.5
1929	94,489	48,565	48.7

[11] F. L. Vaughn, Economics of our patent system, New York, Macmillan, 1925, 198.

About half of the patent applications are refused each year, chiefly on the ground of lack of novelty and anticipation, in view of inventions already patented or described in technical literature. It is folly for any inventor to spend much time or money on a new idea before making an investigation of the technical literature in order to determine what has been done before him. If this were done faithfully by every inventor, there would be very few cases of anticipation and disappointment for him.

Many inventors meet their Waterloo in failing to work out their invention thoroughly and overlooking some important feature. There are many examples in our industrial history. Goodyear, for instance, began to manufacture rubber goods before he thoroughly worked out the process of vulcanization. The manufactured goods soon spoiled in the hands of the dealers and consequently Goodyear was ruined financially. No inventor can dare to overlook any weakness or defects in his invention, for it is certain to be found out in use. Thoroughness is, therefore, absolutely essential, nothing must be taken for granted, every detail must be studied, tested and worked out from all aspects of strength, structure, cost, life, and economy. For these reasons hundreds of thousands of dollars are spent yearly by large companies in perfecting inventions before they make any attempts to market them.

Discouragement is often the worst pitfall of an inventor. In attempting to overcome any or all of the obstacles or pitfalls already enumerated he may simply give up the battle and abandon his invention. This means an economic loss to society because the public never obtains the benefits of his invention which might have been of great utility.

The hope of riches has lured many inventors into pitfalls. Financial reward is, of course, a normal desire but inventors quite often entertain exaggerated notions of the value of their inventions after they are patented expecting each invention will make them multi-millionaires. This may prevent them from reaching any agreements with business men because the sums that they demand are unreasonable. Consequently instead of being satisfied with a moderate compensation, they overreach themselves and lose everything.

It is only natural to be enthusiastic about our creations and to tell others about them. Many inventors have a decided weakness in this direction. In most cases this is a dangerous thing to do unless proper legal steps and precautions have been taken. The inopportune disclosure of an invention to an unscrupulous person may lead to its loss. The inventor can be fleeced in more ways than one by various legal tricks if he is not careful.

The list of patentees published each year by the Government has been termed the "suckers list." Every time an inventor obtains a patent he receives a flood of letters from schemers, dishonest promotors and patent brokers who congratulate him and tell him how rich he will become if he will follow their advice. Some of the cleverest and subtlest schemes have been devised by these men to trick the inventor. Their literature is voluminous, colorful, and attractive. They can usually be detected because sooner or later they will ask for fees ranging from five dollars up to whatever amount they can extract from their victims and will undertake and even guarantee the successful exploitation of an invention. Some of these schemes are described by Milton Wright in his book "Inventions and Patents" as follows:

"One man writes to tell you that your patent is not a good one, but that if you will pay him a certain fee he will have the defects remedied.

"Another advises you that your patent is valuable and that it will make money for you if it is introduced properly. The rights for this State, he says, are worth a certain sum, and for that State another sum. If you will advance him a small amount—anywhere from $10 to $50 —he will have the necessary advertising circulars printed, and your patent will be as good as sold. Sometimes this offer is varied to make it sound more plausible. An odd sum of money is asked for, say, $1.90 for postage and $5.50 for printing, in order to send information to a list of manufacturers who, he tells you, are on the lookout for just such inventions as yours, which they can buy for prices that will seem handsome to you. The odd sum of money, $7.40, somehow makes the scheme sound more genuine than if round figures were used.

"One company, with a name that sounds impressive, offers to insure your patent for a short time only against infringers. You pay $8 within thirty days and you get 'pat insurance' for a year. As a matter of fact, there is little likelihood that there is going to be any infringement in that time, and even if there should be, you probably would find it mighty hard to collect anything from the man who is so anxious to collect your 'premium.' This applies only to some insurers, however. Really substantial and sincere concerns have tried patent insurance and have met with a measure of success.

"One man may write you that he has an actual offer of $100,000 for the patent rights for Canada. He says he will take out a Canadian patent for you as soon as you send him the fee. But when the Canadian patent has been obtained, the prospective purchaser has changed his mind.

"A scheme, a little more complicated, is this: A firm purporting to be manufacturers sends you a letter inquiring what price you ask for your patent. You reply, saying $10,000. Then another firm, supposed to be the agents of the pretended manufacturers, writes you that the 'manufacturers' have decided to accept your offer, provided your title and claims are examined and found to be all right. The agents ask that you send $50 for the examination. If you send it, an unfavorable report is made, and you have nothing to show for your $50 but your experience. This scheme has several variations.

"Another used extensively is that of the so-called patent engineer. You are advised that a survey should be made showing the value of your invention and how it will meet the needs of the market. The company offers to give you this survey with an impressive report and explains to you that such a report will enable you to sell your patent more readily. Such a survey and report might be highly desirable if it were actually made; but when it is ready-made and is passed out to you on payment of a fee—usually $25—it, of course, has no value whatever; it is only another way of spending $25. The fee, by the way, in such cases is not paid in advance, but only upon receipt of the impressive-looking 'report.' "[12]

A volume could be written on the obstacles and pitfalls encountered by inventors. In this chapter we have only attempted to touch the high lights of this subject which is of very great psychological significance to the inventor.

[12] M. Wright, Inventions and patents, New York, McGraw-Hill, 1927, 61-63.

CHAPTER XII

Heredity and Invention *

THE INFLUENCE of environment and heredity on human achievement is a problem which has aroused considerable discussion, research and thought, but no evidence has yet been found which definitely points to heredity or environment as the deciding factor. The position taken by many students today is that heredity and environment are complementary factors, each one being a different phase of the same problem depending on the viewpoint. We no longer set heredity above environment but regard each in terms of the other. There is no question that heredity and environment interact to produce the characteristics of all individuals. Both carry with them certain limitations beyond which the individual cannot go. The biologists tend to regard heredity as a limiting factor for the possible education obtainable by training. However, nature and nurture are really mutually inclusive. The environmental forces react on the hereditary tendencies and produce their effects by mutual interaction.

The question whether inventiveness is inherited reduces itself to the problem of the inheritance of mental capacities, tendencies and abilities. No one will deny that organic structures are inherited, but is such a specific ability as inventing inheritable? All persons unquestionably inherit certain capacities and tendencies such as the sensory capacities, the instincts or unlearned responses and reflexes.

Many workers in heredity have attempted to show that some special abilities, such as mechanical ability, artistic

---

* Reprinted with additions from the Journal of Heredity, December, 1930, by J. Rossman.

ability, judicial and military ability are inherited. The outstanding study was made by Galton [1] embracing a group of 977 eminent men and their relatives. This group of eminent men had 739 relatives of eminence including 50 grandfathers, 94 fathers, 54 uncles, 123 brothers, 66 nephews, 145 sons and 42 grandsons. Other studies have been made by Woods [2] on 671 members of royalty; Havelock Ellis [3] studied 1,030 British men and women of genius; Cattell [4] and Brimhall [5] made a study of American men of science. Studies have also been made by Clarke,[6] and de Candolle [7] showing that eminence runs in the same families.

It is also possible to determine the ancestry of eminent persons by a study of the social class from which they come. Galton has shown that the great majority of Englishmen of science came from professional classes as follows:

	Per cent
Nobility and gentlemen	9
Military and government	18
Professional	34
Commerce	43
Farmers	2
Others	1
Total	107 (11 duplicates)

Ellis found the ancestry of the eminent men and women was as follows:

[1] F. Galton, Hereditary genius, New York, Appleton, 1869, reprint 1914.

[2] F. A. Woods, Mental and moral heredity in royalty, New York, Holt, 1906.

[3] H. Ellis, A study of British genius, London, Hurst and Blackett, 1904.

[4] J. M. Cattell, American men of science, Garrison, Science Press, 1921. A statistical study of American men of Science, 1906, N. S. 24, 732-744. A statistical study of eminent men, Popular Science Monthly, 1903, 62, 359-377.

[5] D. R. Brimhall, Family resemblances among American men of science, American Naturalist, 1922, 56, 504-547; Vol. 57, 1923, 74-88, 137-152, 326-344.

[6] E. L. Clarke, American men of letters, Studies in History, Economics, and Public Law, No. 168, Columbia Univ. 1916.

[7] A. De Candolle, Histoire des sciences et des savants depuis deux siècles, 2d ed., Genève-Bale, Georg, 1885.

	Per cent
Professions	35.2
Upper classes, officials, army and navy	27.8
Commercial	18.8
Crafts, artisans, unskilled	11.7
Yeomen and farmers	6.0

Cattell's study of American men of science showed their fathers to be of the following classes:

	Per cent
Professional	43.1 (3.0 per cent in general population)
Commercial	35.7 (34.1 per cent in general population)
Agriculture	21.2 (41.1 per cent in general population)

These findings do not necessarily mean that heredity is the sole cause of eminence. Children born in eminent families inherit not only their organic mechanism from their parents but also their social environment. The Bach children were born in a musical environment and were under the constant stimulation of music. This might have been decidedly more important than their organic heredity.

Bogardus analyzes the fundamental conditions essential to genius and achievement as follows:

"1. A social environment which is mentally stimulating. Genius rarely matures under a widespread pall of mental stagnation. There must be mental contacts which strike fire and some general appreciation of achievements that a genius can effect.

"2. Thorough training. There are only a few successful persons today who have not spent time and energy in developing and perfecting techniques. It is becoming increasingly true that special ability must have a commensurate scholastic and practical training as a basis for complete self-expression. It is fair to assume that the greater the potential ability the greater will be the value of both extensive and intensive training. Nearly all accredited geniuses, whether of the Paderewski or the Edison type, report that many hours daily are spent in 'practice' and hence in training. In order that all the special abilities of a person may be fully developed, his education must begin early, proceed as systematically as possible, and be continued throughout life. The greater the genius the more imperative is a thorough training.

"3. Freedom from the struggle for bread. If energy is continually expended in securing the necessities of life, genius is to that extent hampered. Sufficient means for travel and research is another essential.

"4. Social respect as a medium for the development of self-respect. Persons with special talent are often a thermometer of the social reflections of themselves. A genius is handicapped if he grows up as a member of a race that is despised by a dominant race, in a community where luxury spreads an enervating virus, or where vice in any form destroys the energies of life." [8]

In order to throw some light on the heredity of inventiveness, the inventors of this study were requested to give the occupation of their father. The results are given in Table 15.

TABLE 15
OCCUPATION OF THE FATHERS OF 710 INVENTORS

Occupation	Number	Per cent	Occupation	Number	Per cent
Professional	*231*	*33.3*	*Commercial*	*246*	*35.5*
Engineer	46		Merchant	129	
Attorney	31		Manufacturer	62	
Educator	26		Superintendent	27	
Physician	25		Contractor	19	
Musician & Artist	24		Salesman	9	
Clergyman	23		*Skilled labor*	*112*	*16.2*
Public Official	20		Trades	80	
Banker	13		Mechanic	32	
Chemist & Pharmacist	12		*Agriculture*	*104*	*15.0*
Mathematician	6		Farmer	104	
Publisher, Writer	5		*No answer*	*17*	

[8] E. S. Bogardus, Fundamentals of social psychology, New York, Century, 1924, 387-388.

Table 15 shows that about one-third of the inventors had fathers engaged in the professions, 35.5 per cent of the fathers were engaged in commercial activities, 16.2 per cent were skilled laborers, 15 per cent were farmers. The occupation of the fathers shows that the inventors of this study come from a decidedly superior stock. It may be, of course, that the homes of engineers, physicians, attorneys, clergymen and educators are extremely favorable to the child for the expression of originality as well as in affording excellent opportunities for study and schooling.

The Army tests have shown that there are distinct differences in the intelligence of the various occupational groups. The professional groups such as doctors, engineers, lawyers, were at the top in the scores made; whereas laborers, farmers, painters, traders were at the bottom. According to Ellis: "The Army tests were given to adults, mostly young, who were actually engaged in particular occupations. Very similar results, however, have been secured by studies made on children classified by the occupation of their parents. Studies along this line are rather numerous, but a few will be given to illustrate the results. Duff and Thomson [9] tested 13,419 children, 11 and 12 years of age, in England and classified these according to parental occupation. The average I. Q. for children of the professional classes was 112.2 and for laborers 96. Other occupational groups were between these. Pressey and Ralston [10] tested all the available children from 10 to 14 years of age in a town of 12,000, these being 548 in number, and found that 85 per cent of the children of professional men were above the median of the total group in comparison with 68 per cent of the children of artisans, and 39 per cent of the children

[9] J. F. Duff and G. H. Thomson, The social and geographical distribution of intelligence in Northumberland, British Journal of Psychology, Gen. Sec., 1923, 14, 192-198.

[10] S. L. Pressey and R. Ralston, The relation of the general intelligence of school children to the occupation of their fathers, Journal of Educational Psychology, 1919, 3, 366-373.

of the laborers. Dexter [11] tested children in grades 1 to 8 in 13 ward schools in Madison, Wisconsin, and determined the average scores for occupational groups. The correlation between this determination and the results of the Army tests was found to be 0.79. Haggerty and Nash [12] studied the intelligence of children according to occupation of parents and found in the elementary school the same general results as those already described. In the high school the differences were not pronounced, but great differences were found in the amount of selection occurring before high school. A much smaller per cent of the children of the laboring classes attend high school. A rather large difference was found between the children of miners and those of lawyers. None of the former group attained the median attained by the latter group. Generally speaking, there is, of course, much overlapping between the various groups." [13]

If we are to accept the general results of these studies we must then conclude that the inventors of our study are highly intelligent as they come from the upper groups of the population.

The inventors of this study were also asked to state whether their children showed any evidence of inventiveness. The results are given in Table 16.

TABLE 16

INVENTIVENESS OF THE CHILDREN OF INVENTORS

Traits shown	Number
Inventive	296
Not inventive	151
No children	96
Too young	88
No answers	79
Total	710

[11] E. S. Dexter, Relation between occupation of parents and intelligence of children, School and Society, 1923, 17, 612-616.

[12] M. E. Haggerty and H. B. Nash, Mental capacity of children and paternal occupation, Journal of Educational Psychology, 1924, 15, 559-572.

[13] R. S. Ellis, The psychology of individual differences, New York, Appleton, 1928, 390-391.

Table 16 shows that 66.4 per cent of the inventors having grown up children indicated that their children showed some evidence of inventiveness. It is difficult to determine just what standards were used in answering this question but the test used generally was one of originality and individuality in their activities.

A study was also made of the inventiveness of the relations of the inventors. The results are given in Table 17 together with the answers reported for the inventiveness of the children of the inventors.

TABLE 17

INVENTIVE RELATIVES OF INVENTORS AND INVENTIVENESS OF THE CHILDREN OF THE INVENTORS

Relationship	Totals	Inventiveness of children of inventors				
		Inventive	No. of inventors per child	Not inventive	No. of inventors per child	No answer
Ancestors	*189*	*102*	*1.9*	*13*	*14.5*	*74*
Father	108	58		2		48
Mother	7	4		1		2
Grandparents	74	40		10		24
Other relatives	*91*	*41*	*2.2*	*19*	*4.8*	*31*
Uncles	29	13		2		14
Cousins	22	10		7		5
Brothers	34	15		10		9
Other remote relatives	6	3				3
Sub. Total	*280*	*143*	*1.9*	*32*	*8.7*	*105*
No relatives	430	153	2.8	119	3.6	158
Total	*710*	*296*		*151*		*263*

Nearly forty per cent of the inventors had relatives who were inventors. These inventors had 143 children who showed evidence of inventiveness or 48.3 per cent of all the children reported as showing inventiveness by 710 inventors. Table 17 appears to show that the nearer the relatives who are inventors the more the children tend to show inventiveness. Thus there were 189 inventors who had direct inventive ancestors and had 102 inventive children and 13 no inventive children. There were 91 inventors who had 41 inventive children and 19 non-inventive children. In other words for each 1.9 inventors who had direct inventive ancestors there was one inventive child, whereas 2.2 inventors who had more remote inventive relatives were required for one inventive child. Likewise it took 14.5 inventors having direct inventive ancestors to produce one non-inventive child, against 4.8 inventors who had more remote inventive relatives.

A comparison of all inventors who had inventive relatives with inventors who had no inventive relatives also shows decided differences in the inventiveness of their children. Thus there are 1.9 inventors having inventive relatives for each inventive child, against 2.8 inventors having no inventive relatives for each inventive child. There are also 8.7 inventors having inventive relatives for each non-inventive child, against 3.6 inventors having no inventive relatives for each non-inventive child.

The problem of individual heredity of inventiveness also raises the question whether there is such a thing as racial heredity of inventiveness. A study of the geographic distribution of inventors tends to show that they are found in greater numbers in proportion to the population in certain regions both in the United States and Europe than in other regions. We find, for example, that the Pacific, New England, Middle Atlantic and North Central States are considerably higher in inventiveness than the South Atlantic or Central States. In Europe, Switzerland and the northern and western countries such as England, Norway, Germany, France, are superior in inventiveness to the southern and eastern countries such as Italy, Spain, Turkey and Russia. Whether this is due to economic conditions or to the racial stock is difficult to determine. The sharp differences in distribution might have been caused by shifts in the population, the more able, progressive and intelligent members of the population moving to more favorable regions. This may be a plausible explanation for the distribution in the United States. As to racial distributions there may be race degeneration, unfavorable geographic conditions which prevent industrialization. These possible causes, however, are mere conjectures.

Bernard states: "It is not possible now to settle finally the question of relative inherited race superiority and inferiority. But it may be well to note that psychologists and sociologists are inclined to attribute differences in intelligence between the races more to cultural transmission or 'social heredity' than to chromosome transmission or biological heredity. However, there may well be minor differences in intelligence due to inheritance. If it can be shown, as some anthropologists believe, that racial differences depend largely on inherited differences in endocrine supply and distribution, this difference in endocrines might conceivably reflect itself in intelligence levels, although we have at present little or no direct evidence to support such a theory. If differences in neural structure could be established between the members of any two races this fact might lead to the same general conclusion. But endocrine differences might be expected more easily to lead to differences in emotional attitude and expression. Whether the different emotional attitudes of various races can be traced to such a cause or whether they are dependent upon different conditions of living and different customs and traditions we cannot now say. Southern peoples are more expressive of their emotions, are of a more active temperament, gesticulate and exclaim more than northern peoples. But this may be the result of their constant outdoor life which leads to much association and interstimulation and the constant need for adjustment. Their religion also seems to be less intellectual and more ritualistic, and they also have more illiteracy. Perhaps their more general habits of submitting to autocratic government in spite of their impulsive dispositions may also go back to the matter of education, or the lack of it.

"Race is, after all, primarily an abstract synthetic concept, a class term, used to symbolize a conceptual synthesis of a great many characteristics which we more or less arbitrarily agree to call collectively by some specific race name. Its unity is merely an abstraction existing as a statistical means or average in our own minds without concrete objective reality. There is no one person in a so-called race who is wholly typical of our abstract and synthetic concept of that race. Nor do we find any conclusive unity or identity of traits in the various members of a so-called race. Always the extremes of traits within a race show greater differences than do the means of any two races. Also there are large numbers of a people whom it is impossible to classify definitely and scientifically within one race as against another, except on arbitrary grounds. Thus we classify in this country as Negro any person known to have traces of Negro 'blood,' even though only a small proportion of his inheritance may have come from Negro ancestry. Race is therefore primarily an abstract statistical concept, based on averages of certain isolable traits, and not a concrete biological and psychological fact. It is a collective or social concept, but it is not wholly divorced from concrete biological traits. In fact the statistical average is built up around a synthesis of concrete biological traits. These constitute the basis of race distinctions. Recognized as such, race is an effective social symbol by means of which we control human relationships and compel collective adjustments on a wide scale. As an abstract or conceptual social phenomenon race is very real. So also is race prejudice, which is a psycho-social phenomenon growing out of our abstract synthetic concept of race and reinforced by it. Not all realities are biological and concrete. Some are abstract and social. And the latter may be as powerful for control purposes as the former. But we should not confuse an abstract conceptual social fact with a concrete biological one in our thinking." [14]

The upshot of all the racial studies made up to the present time makes it impossible to evaluate races by their inventiveness or the number of their eminent men. As Cooley has said: "I trust I have made clear my reassons for thinking that estimates of the worth of races based upon the number and trade of the eminent men they produce, have no scientific justification unless it be possible to eliminate those social conditions that have quite as much to do with the matter as a race. That such elimination is usually impossible, I suppose all will admit. To show, in a general way, the power of historical forces is easy, but to take exact account of them, to predict their future operation, to show just how they differ in different times and countries, and how much must be allowed for that difference, is, in the present state of historical science, quite out of the question. If, however, cases can be found where two races mingle and compete in the same order, and under conditions substantially the same, a valuable comparison might perhaps be made." [15]

Tozzer in summing up the question of the mentality of different races states that "It should be borne in mind that it is not possible to prove the question one way or the other if scientific data are demanded on which to base a decision. *A priori*, one can say that there seems to be some reason to think that the Negro race as a whole fails to measure up to the intellectual standard of the other two great groups of mankind, the White and the Mongolian. If, however, we free our minds as much as possible from prejudice, and take into consideration the emotional factor present in our decision, we should hesitate to deny that many of the deficiencies of the Negro are due not to an intellectual capacity, but to a social

[14] L. L. Bernard, An introduction to social psychology, New York, Holt, 1926, 231-236.

[15] C. H. Cooley, Genius, fame and the comparison of races, Annals of the American Academy of Political and Social Science, 1897, 9, 317-358.

and to a lesser extent, physical environment which are decidedly unfavorable." [16]

Practically every civilization in the past has made some contribution to the field of invention which has been passed on to succeeding ages. Thus, what the world received in the field of science from Arabian sources is indicated by the retention in our vocabulary of such words as: alchemy, alcohol, alembic, algebra, alkali, almanac, azimuth, chemistry, elixir, zenith, nadir.

In the manufacturing line names of eastern places have been given to various fabrics and other articles, as for instance: "Muslin" comes from Mosul; "Damask" from Damascus; "Gauze" from Gaza; Damascus and Toledo blades show the proficiency of the Arabs in metallurgy, while the "Zero" which is the symbol employed in their numerical system is used in our own system, known as the Arabic or Decimal System, which has given the world an indispensable means for all scientific investigation dependent upon mathematical calculation.

It is conceded by all students that China has developed in the past an extremely high type of civilization. It unquestionably produced a very high class of inventive genius. It may be useful to enumerate some of the inventions listed by a Chinese engineer Chung-Yee Wang: "The compass: Records show that Chow Kung in the Chow Dynasty, about 1122 B. C. used a kind of wagon equipped with an instrument that pointed always toward the north.

"Paper was first made by Tsai Lun, out of tree fibers, rags and hemp, during the Dynasty of Eastern Han, the early part of the first century.

"Printing: It has been mentioned that Fung To originated the art of stereotyped wooden plates about the year 932 A.D., but later investigation made by the sinologue Stanislas Julien has shown that the invention actually dated from the year 593. A record of this period proves

[16] A. F. Tozzer, Social origins and social continuities, New York, Macmillan, 1926, 79.

this: 'It was decreed that drawings and unpublished texts should be collected and engraved on wood for publication.'

"Glass was first manufactured by Pun Fang about the early part of the second century. It is recorded that he had a piece carved with 130 designs.

"Seismograph: An instrument, resembling perhaps the present day seismograph was invented by Chang Heng in the first century, during the Han Dynasty, which could record any slight earthquake not perceptible by human senses.

"Metals: In Tai Hao's time (2852-2737 B. C.) metallic coin was already in circulation. The inventive genius of the ancient Chinese can nowhere be more explicitly shown than in the art of making alloys. An alloy, similar to German silver, under the name of Pait' ong, was obtained by fusing 'red steel' with arsenic. The manufacture by the ancients of gongs and tom toms, with their chemical composition has been determined.

"Medicine: We may laugh at some of the ridiculous prescriptions of Chinese doctors; but I believe that there is a great deal of Chinese medicine that is both useful and illuminating when viewed in the light of occidental medical science. The Chinese anesthetic, known as Ma Fat powder, a sort of hashish, was discovered by the famous Chinese surgeon, Hwa To, who lived in the early part of the second century, during the Eastern Han Dynasty. An old Chinese text tells us that Hwa To administered the medicine to his patients to render them unconscious before being operated upon. This happened long before ether or chloroform was discovered in Europe.

"Recently two experiments at the Rockefeller Medical Institute in New York City obtained a white secretion which they had named Bufin, by stimulating the paratid gland of the toad by means of electricity. Its physiological action is almost similar to that of digitalis. This is merely a rediscovery of a medicine long known in China. The identical white secretion is obtained today by the

Chinese by touching the biggest wart-like swelling just behind the eye of a toad with a hot iron. The secretions thus obtained from many toads are allowed to evaporate slowly to a powder, which is now mainly used as a heart remedy."[17]

Why has the inventive genius of China disappeared and why has she declined in all other social aspects? The answer is probably ancestor worship, the reign of conservatism and blind prejudice for many centuries with the resultant deterioration of ideals. "For example, the premium of the old state-examination system of China put upon the writings of certain thinkers who lived long before our era tended to shackle the original minds of each generation. The embryo Pasteur or Edison was so intimidated by the universal opinion that wisdom died with the sages so that he could bring forth nothing. Thus the social atmosphere lost the stimulating ozone it had in the old inspiring days when the Chinese invented gunpowder, block-printing, banknotes, porcelain, the compass, the compartment boat and the taxicab."[18]

The data presented in this chapter indicate that the transmission of inventive ability involves numerous factors which at present are difficult to evaluate. Economic and geographic conditions and social ideals may be the chief causes for the decided differences in the geographic distribution of inventiveness rather than any innate hereditary abilities. Further study is necessary before this question can be satisfactorily answered.

---

[17] Popular research narratives, Baltimore, Williams & Wilkins, 1926, Vol. 2, 78-80.

[18] E. A. Ross, Principles of sociology, New York, Century, 1920, 675.

CHAPTER XIII

Psychological Theories of Invention

THE psychological theories which have been advanced to explain invention are attempts to reduce the entire process to a single generalization, or formula. We have seen in Chapters V and VI that the actual, as well as the mental processes in inventing, are highly complex, embracing nearly all the psychological aspects of human behavior and with our present knowledge it would be impossible to summarize the process of invention in a simple generalization. However, it will be interesting to review briefly some of the proposed theories, for every theory, after all, contains a grain of truth.

THE "GESTALT" THEORY OF INVENTION

The "Gestalt" view of invention regards every act of invention as the completion of a pattern or configuration which was previously recognized as being incomplete. An excellent statement of this view has been recently made by Usher: "Invention finds its distinctive feature in the constructive assimilation of preexisting elements into new syntheses, new patterns, or new configurations of behavior. The objectives may vary through a wide range: including at one extreme, creations intended to gratify æsthetic desires; and at the other, mechanical devices for the more facile gratification of material wants. Invention thus established relationships that did not previously exist. In its barest essence, the element of innovation lies in the completion of an incomplete pattern of behavior or in the improvement of a pattern that was unsatisfactory and inadequate. Innovation of this type appears in its lowest form in the learning of an act of skill which may not require any implements at all. Some significant innovation in behavior occurs when the directness of action characteristic of the wholly naive animal is qualified by the power to substitute roundabout methods whenever the direct method of gratification is obstructed." [1]

It has been long recognized that inventions consist of new combinations or groupings of known elements. An examination and slight study of almost any invention will readily show this to be true. The Gestalt view thus makes no new contribution to the psychological problems involved in invention and it merely expresses a well-known truth from a slightly different viewpoint.

Usher, however, realizes the complex factors involved in invention when he states that "our mental processes fall in two types; the synthetic, constructive, and creative activities concerned with innovation; the analytical, imitative, and conservative activities concerned with the formulation and imposition of tradition. A comprehensive theory of innovation would involve by necessity all the synthetic activities, but it could not be confined to them because the analytical activities are called into play at several stages in the process. The data of experience must be organized and worked into consciously defined configurations or patterns. Some of these achievements in organization may obstruct particular innovations, but on the whole the enlargement of our significant experience is dependent upon systematic analysis and organization. The unorganized content of the mind also plays an important part in innovation, and thus consideration of perception, memory and imitation becomes an essential part of the study of innovation. Because the impulses to invention and discovery are deeply involved in the emotions, a comprehensive account must of necessity include the study of the emotional life from this special point of view. The innovating activities of the mind are

---

[1] A. P. Usher, A history of mechanical invention, New York, McGraw-Hill, 1929, 11.

thus synthetic not merely as regards the form in which their results are expressed. They are a synthesis of all the faculties of conscious life. Strictly speaking, any adequate theory of innovation would be an analysis of all the activities of the mind from a somewhat special point of view." [2]

We have seen in Chapters V and VI that invention is an integral part of the learning process and that not only the synthetic but the analytic mental processes are involved in inventing. We have also seen that the emotional background is a highly important factor and in inventing all the activities of the mind must be studied from a special point of view.

THE SUBCONSCIOUS THEORY

The sudden flashes and so-called inspirations and happy thoughts which many creative workers experience have been chiefly responsible for the many mystical explanations of originality and invention. These experiences appear to have no immediate cause and they have therefore led many people to attribute them to some force existing outside of themselves such as external intelligence or God. An analysis of these inspirations will ultimately show that they have a definite origin in previous experiences. But even admitting this to be true, the formation of new mental patterns or combinations seems to be caused by some mysterious mental activity. Not knowing how they occur, they have been readily explained by stating that they are the work of the subconscious. It is a general human weakness to give names to things or processes we do not understand and then to accept these names as final explanations. The subconscious is one of these names. According to this view the wishes which cannot be gratified in the conscious mind take up their abode in the subconscious mind where they initiate

[2] A. P. Usher, A history of mechanical invention, New York, McGraw-Hill, 1929, 9-10.

a thinking process analogous to an uncontrolled reverie or day-dream which might be considered as a kind of lower thinking as compared with the critical and controlled conscious thinking. It is uncontrolled thinking which is responsible for the formation of new patterns which are then passed on to the conscious mind for criticism in these sudden flashes or inspirations.

Not all psychologists will agree that our minds can be divided into different levels but they rather believe there is only one kind of mental activity. Undoubtedly some sort of mental activity is going on during the inventive process of which the inventor is not always conscious as we have seen in Chapter VI, but referring this merely to the subconscious as an explanation merely begs the question.

We have already seen that the desire to satisfy a need and the emotional reaction produced by this striving initiates a neural process which eventuates in the formation of a satisfactory mental pattern. This view is supported by the work of such neurologists as Herrick who was quoted in Chapter VI.

INVENTION AS SELF-EXPRESSION

The desire for self-expression and superiority have also been given as the causes for invention and especially as the main motives leading to invention. "Take the child who finds he is at a disadvantage in some respect in his relations with his playmates. Perhaps he is so frail that he cannot participate in the rough games in which most strong children indulge. Instead of brooding over his handicap and upsetting himself emotionally, he takes to books and outshines the other children in the classrooms. John Richard Green, the historian, was so sickly as a boy that play held little charm for him. Cut off from the physically active side of life, he learned to find his delight in books. Similarly, James Watt, realizing that he was too delicate to enter sports, grew fond of study, reflection and solitude. Scholastic superiority gives the frail child something to brag about, wins the praise of his self-respect, an essential element in mental health."[3]

Invention according to this view is caused by the desire for compensating one's inferiority. It is interesting to note that some of our most brilliant inventors, such as Charles P. Steinmetz, had definite physical defects which apparently were no hindrance in their inventing. Inventing as thus regarded is an activity which tends to compensate some personal inferiority or defect.

Allport lays down four criteria of compensatory traits: (1) They originate from an obstacle, defect, or limitation; (2) further adjustment of the individual is effected, not by trying to adapt reality to his own peculiarities, but by adapting his capacities to reality; (3) these activities become not merely so many separate acts of adjustment but prepotent habit trends, or drives, which in time appear as ends in themselves; (4) since these habit trends become controlling forces in themselves, they tend to carry the individual past an adjustment which is simply adequate, to higher levels than he would have attained without the original defect.[4]

It is not to be denied that the compensatory view of invention throws some light on the motivation of the inventor but it sheds little light on the mental processes themselves which are the basis of invention. It is true that invention is a form of expression and individualism, but these are merely connotations of the activity of invention as a phase of human behavior without regard to the mental processes involved.

NECESSITY AS THE CAUSE OF INVENTION

It has been often said that necessity is the cause of invention. This is only the expression of a half truth be-

---

[3] W. F. Vaughan, The lure of superiority, New York, Holt, 1928, vii.

[4] F. H. Allport, Social psychology, Boston Houghton, Mifflin Co., 1924, 115.

cause not all necessities have been immediately followed by the needed inventions. Many much needed inventions have waited for centuries before they were invented. Take the plough, for instance. For numerous centuries man was badly in need of a good plough as his existence depended to a great extent on his agricultural activities. Yet this need was not supplied until comparatively recent times when Charles Newbold invented in 1797 a plough made from solid iron except the beam and handles. Necessity alone was not sufficient to supply the need. It is true, however, that necessity as an external stimulus, if sufficiently experienced by an inventor as we have seen in Chapter VI will produce invention.

This has been well expressed by the famous inventor Marconi: "Necessity is the cause of many inventions but the best ones are born of desire. One says, 'I wish I could' do this or that and then tries it. They arise out of dissatisfaction with apparent limitations of life, and the apparent rules that hamper comfort, success or enjoyment. Fulton said 'I wish I could run a boat with an engine,' and did it. Before him Stephenson said 'I wish I could use the power of steam, and did that,' Morse wished to transmit signals over a wire, Bell wished to make those signals carry speech, Edison wished to record and reproduce them. There was no necessity but there was vision.

"All people meet these necessities and have these visions. They occur constantly in every line of activity. Most inventions go knocking at many brains before the door in some mind opens to receive them. The inventive mind—the 'resourceful' mind meets these needs or visions freshly and either makes sure that the routine answer is the right one or invents a new answer on the spot. The difference, in the long run, is the difference between success and failure. In most pursuits, indeed, the degree of a man's inventiveness will almost exactly measure his success." [5]

---

[5] G. Marconi, Every man his own inventor, Colliers, 1922, 70, 5-6.

Necessities may be roughly divided into external and internal. The internal necessities such as hunger or thirst bring immediate and direct action. As direct action becomes impossible the efforts to satisfy the desires becomes more indirect by means of inventions. The external necessities are represented by such needs as shelter, refuge from the elements or danger of beasts. Mason has aptly said "The evolution of human wants, . . . is a part of the history of invention." [6]

We have seen that inventions are a response to wants. The means by which these wants are satisfied depend to a great extent on the geographic environment of the individual. Nature must always supply the raw materials to the inventor and the type of the inventions made depends on the materials available.

We have a striking illustration of the influence of the environment in the case of the Eskimos who have developed many inventions conditioned by their surroundings. "Windows without glass, the carpenter's brace, the first decked boat, a type of self-supporting vault unknown to civilized architecture, an artificial arm, are only a few of the achievements to the credit of the Eskimo; while he has solved the problem of drilling a curved hole, or sawing without a saw with ease.

"With the exception of but a few tribes, they live in a climate where wood and all the products of the vegetable kingdom are unknown, except perhaps for such small quantities as the ocean currents may drift to their shores. One half the mineral substances, including the all-important metals, are also beyond their reach in the ever frozen north; even if they mined ore, they would not have the fuel to smelt it. Only products of animal origin—bone, skin, hair, and ivory—stone and the elemental substances ice, snow, and water, are at their service.

"The snow-house well illustrates this. The Romans and their predecessors worked out the true arch and vault, and the Mayas of Yucatan the false arch, but the

[6] O. T. Mason, The origins of invention, London, W. Scott, 1895, 19.

Eskimo builds a spiral vault, which needs no scaffolding. . . ." [7]

Inventions were at first made to supply man's basic wants but as these wants were satisfied by inventions, the inventions themselves gave rise to new needs in so far as attempts were made to improve them. Most of our inventions today are actually made to meet the needs caused by existing inventions. It is for this reason that the effects of inventions are cumulative for they are caused by the permutative multiplication of inventions. As the number of inventions increases, the possibility of new combinations increases so that further inventions are made. This principle has been recognized by Iles who states that: "We shall find that the principle of permutation accounts . . . in large measure for three cardinal facts in the history of man: First, his leaps forward; second, the constant accelerations in these leaps; and third, the gap in the record of the tribes which, in the illimitable past, have succumbed as forces of a new edge and sweep have become engaged in the fray." [8]

THE INSTINCT OF WORKMANSHIP

The instinct of workmanship has been proposed by Veblen as an explanation for invention. In the days when his book appeared "instincts" were used to explain everything about which we knew nothing. Veblen's theory briefly states that the instinct of contrivance is native to human beings and is the chief cause for the inventive activity of man.

Veblen defines his term as follows: "In making use of the expression 'instinct of workmanship' it is not intended to assume or to argue that the proclivity so designated is in the psychological respect a simple or irreducible element; still less is there any intention to allege that it is to be traced back in the physiological respect to

[7] A. L. Kroeber, The Eskimos as aboriginal inventors, Scientific American, 1914, 110, 54.

[8] G. Iles, Flame, electricity and the camera, New York, Doubleday, 1901, 6-7.

some one isolable tropismatic sensibility or some single enzymotic or visceral stimulus . . . The expression may be taken to signify a concurrence of several instinctive aptitudes, each of which might or might not prove simple or irreducible when subjected to psychological or physiological analysis . . . In human behavior this disposition is effective in such consistent, ubiquitous, and resilient fashion that students of human nature will have to count it as one of the integral hereditary traits of mankind. . . .

"Much of the functional content of the instinct of workmanship is a proclivity for taking pains. The best or most finished outcome of this disposition is not had under stress of great excitement or under extreme urgency from any of the instinctive propensities with which its work is associated or whose ends it serves. It shows at its best, both in the individual workman's technological efficiency and in the growth of technological proficiency and insight in the community at large, under circumstances of moderate exigence, where there is work at hand and more of it in sight, since it is initially a disposition to do the next thing and do it as well as may be; whereas when interest falls off unduly through failure of provocation from the instinctive dispositions that afford an end to which to work, the stimulus to workmanship is likely to fail, and the outcome is as likely to be an endless fabrication of meaningless details and much ado about nothing. On the other hand, in seasons of great stress, when the call to any one or more of the instinctive lines of conduct is urgent beyond measure, there is likely to result a crudity of technique and presently a loss of proficiency and technological mastery." [9]

From this quotation we can at once see the Veblen uses the term "instinct" in a very loose sense and that his definition of the instinct of contrivance is merely an-

---

[9] T. Veblen, The instinct of workmanship, New York, Macmillan, 1914, 27-34.

other term for man's entire activity as an inventor. Strictly speaking instinctive behavior is unlearned, inherited behavior and in this sense the instinct of contrivance does not exist. Inventing is a learned behavior and there is no evidence whatsoever to indicate that it is instinctive.

BEHAVIORISTIC VIEW OF INVENTION

The behaviorist's formula for all human behavior is dependent on the stimulus and response situation. Inventions are accordingly merely a phase of the response of human beings to stimuli which exist in man's environment. Actual physical needs, the cultural state of knowledge, the conditions aroused by competition in industry, defects in existing inventions are stimuli which produce invention. Invention is thus man's attempt to adapt himself to his environment whether it is physical or social in nature.

Watson believes that Veblen's instinct of contrivance is really dependent on the instinctive tendency of manipulation found in all human beings. "That there is an original tendency to reach out for objects, to scrape them along the floor, to pick them up, put them into the mouth, to throw them upon the floor, to move back and forth any parts which can be moved, is one of the best grounded and best observed of the instincts. From our point of view this instinct to manipulate, even though it must be supplemented, as we brought out above, by certain habit factors, is probably the most important of all original tendencies in view of the fact that nearly all later habit formations are dependent upon it. When we say most important here, we are neglecting for the moment the instincts connected with bodily functions, as sex, the eliminative functions, etc. Curiosity is often listed as one of the important human instincts. The activities seen in curiosity are embraced in those connected with manipulation." [10]

---

[10] J. B. Watson, Psychology from the standpoint of a behaviorist, Phila., Lippincott, 1919, 260.

We have seen in Chapter VI that manipulation is an essential element in invention as it gives the inventor the necessary experience and knowledge which he utilizes in making his inventions. The play of children is one manifestation of the instinct of manipulation. Marconi has sensed this in the following statement: "Boys at play show the whole inventive process at work. There is a flash of inspiration or the development of some need, the search through experiences, and the hope for some method of achieving it, the swift assembling of scraps of knowledge, ideas, and dreams from which a method is evolved, and, finally there is tireless energy in carrying out the plan." [11]

Adults also show an intense pleasure in tinkering and playing with things impelled by mere curiosity without any definite object or goal in view. During this manipulation unexpected results may be obtained which may be of great significance although they were not foreseen or expected. We have seen in Chapter X that the joy of inventing is one of the most powerful motives of inventors. It may be that the intense satisfaction and pleasure derived from inventing is due to the satisfaction of the innate tendency of manipulation.

CHANCE AS A CAUSE OF INVENTION

We have seen that aimless manipulation may lead to invention by pure chance. Some of the basic inventions of primitive man were probably made in this way. The history of some modern inventions shows that chance has been an important factor in their making as we have seen in Chapter VII. In these cases, however, the invention was not produced by aimless manipulation but by the incessant experiments and keen observation of the inventors. Inasmuch as the subject of chance has been already fully covered it will not be necessary to discuss it further here.

---

[11] G. Marconi, Every man his own inventor, Colliers, 1922, 70, 5-6.

THEORY OF IMITATION

A school of sociology was founded by Tarde in which imitation was the basic principle of society. Tarde has gone so far as to include invention as a process of imitation. According to Tarde "every invention resolves itself into the timely intersection in one mind of a current of imitation with another current which re-enforces it, or with an intense perception of some objective fact which throws new light on some old idea, or with the lively experience of a need that finds unhoped for resources in some familiar practice. But if we analyze the feelings and perceptions in question, we shall find that they themselves may be resolved almost entirely, and more and more completely as civilization advances, into psychological elements formed under the influence of example.

"From this point of view several lines of imitation intersected one another in the brilliant eighteenth-century idea of applying the steam-engine, which had already been employed in factories, to the satisfaction of the desire for ocean travel—a desire which had originated through the spread of many antecedent naval inventions. The subsequent adaptation of the screw to the steamboat, both of which had been known of separately for a long time, was a similar idea." [12]

Baldwin has also expressed the view that imitation is the basis of invention. "The child's originalities are in great part the new ways in which he finds his knowledge falling together in consequence of his attempts to act to advantage on what he already knows. Or, made more brief, his originalities arise through his action, struggle, trial of things for himself in an imitative way. The child's originalities, further, are in great measure the combinations of his knowledge which he feels justified in expecting to hold for others to act on also." [13]

---

[12] G. Tarde, The laws of imitation, New York, Holt, 1903, 43-44.
[13] J. M. Baldwin, Social and ethical interpretations in mental development, New York, Macmillan, 1897, 99.

"We may sum up the descriptive account of the child's originalities under a term which is sufficiently general on the one hand, and on the other hand sufficiently popular, by calling them in all cases the child's 'interpretations.' The imitative copy within himself or out in the world is what he interprets; and into his interpretations goes all the wealth of his earlier informations, his habits and his anticipations. The first interpretation is the synthesis which he effects, by his own action, of the new data with his personal growth. But with this first interpretation, as we have seen, he does not rest satisfied. He makes a second interpretation through an appeal to his social fellows, or to his own social judgment. On the basis of the response which he gets, a new synthesis arises constituting his present invention. This is held until the whole mass of elements going to make it up is again precipitated for another interpretation by some new suggestion from the sources of his knowledge. So he never rests, never ceases to invent." [14]

Several writers have seen a striking similarity of man-made inventions with the structures found in nature. Thus Wood states in his preface to "Nature's Teachings" "as existing human inventions have been anticipated by Nature, so it will surely be found that in Nature lie the prototypes of inventions not yet revealed to man. The great discoverers of the future will, therefore, be those who will look to Nature for Art, Science, or Mechanics, instead of taking pride in some new invention, and then finding that it has existed in Nature for countless centuries." [15]

He then goes on to show the close correspondence of many inventions with plant and animal structure. The tail of the fish is the prototype of the rudder, the saw-fish of the saw, the spider-web of the hunting net, the silkworm of the artificial silk, the sutures of the skull of the

---

[14] Ibid., 120.

[15] J. G. Wood, Nature's teachings, London, J. S. Virtue & Co., 1885, Preface.

dovetail joint, and so on. We have already seen in Chapter VII that inventions have practically never been made by imitating nature. Our inventions may resemble the structures found in nature because we are necessarily limited by the same physical laws. The camera and the eye depend on the same physical principles but the invention of the camera was made with the utter disregard of the structure of the eye. Invention is not a question of imitation but it is rather a mental process which synthesizes the experience of the inventor in order to meet a need. Of course, the inventor may take hints from nature but unless these suggestions initiate the inventive process no invention will be made.

"By laying too much stress upon the notion that the human race has borrowed all its plans and methods from Nature one is apt to forget that the best of instruction has no effect on dull pupils, as every pedagogue will testify. The forms and movements of all things terrestrial were lying before the senses of animated nature for milleniums before our race arrived. How very few of them aroused the apperception of the brute, and stimulated him to those never-ceasing changes which constitute the life of progress. The profound teaching of Nature fell upon those who having ears, heard not." [16]

THE INVENTIVE FACULTY

Another explanation of invention akin to the instinct of contrivance is the inventive faculty or creative genius. According to this view the inventor makes his inventions because he possesses the faculty to create which is inherited or native. Whatever he does is due to this inventive faculty. The inventor is merely a vehicle for this animal which lives in him. We have already seen in Chapter VI that the inventive faculty is a pure myth. It is merely a name for a process about which a greal deal of mystery has been thrown. The work of modern psychol-

[16] O. T. Mason. The origins of invention, London, W. Scott, 1895, 20.

ogists has entirely overthrown the so-called human faculties because they do not exist. The term "faculty" is merely another convenient term to designate a certain aptitude, ability or activity but there is no evidence to show that specific mental faculties exist.

William H. Smyth, whom we quoted in Chapter V, was far ahead of his contemporaries in realizing that the inventive faculty was a myth. According to his view "the mental process involved in making an invention is analogous to that employed by the child in building with his toy blocks. Conceiving the idea of building some sort of house, he first arranges those which he thinks most suitable for the foundation, and continues by selecting from his store of blocks of various shapes and sizes those which he finds best adapted to form the various parts of the complete structure he has in mind. So too the inventor selects from the store of elementary mechanical parts or combinations with which memory has furnished his mind those which he regards as available for his purpose. The child builds and rebuilds; he changes a block here, and removes or ads a block there; so does the inventor, although in his case the mental operations of selection and arrangement are often so quickly and so automatically performed as to escape even his own observation. The material, too, with which the inventor works is infinitely better adapted to its purpose than are the blocks of the child with their unchangeable shapes and dimensions. It may be hard or soft, hot or cold, pervious or impervious, transparent or opaque, elastic or rigid, fluid or viscous; in short, it may be regarded as infinitely plastic, though possessing every other inherent quality known in nature or art.

When confronted with a defect in his structure, the child is compelled to laboriously select from his heap of blocks, critically examining each one and trying its effect as a part of the whole; but the inventor's mass of material is of a much more manageable character. In an instant the panorama of memory is unfolded, and he makes his selection—a process which may be repeated not merely once, but a hundred times, while the hand of the child would be faltering over a single block. Among this material the mind of the inventor works as a modeler in infinitely plastic clay. With such facilities and such material why should not great results be accomplished? On the contrary, would not he be a bungler indeed who under these conditions should prove to be incapable of producing a worthy result?" [17]

IMAGINATION

We have seen that the mental process termed imagination is one of the important steps in the inventive process; without imagination no invention is possible because the process of imagination represents the synthetic mental activity making new combinations and patterns of past experiences. The formation of new solutions is due to the imagination. It is, therefore, not surprising to find inventors and other creative workers attributing to their imagination the causes for all their creative ability.

We must bear in mind that the term "imagination" is really another faculty term and as such does not exist. The word, however, is convenient in designating a mental process which actually exists and as we have seen is due entirely to the neural activity in the brain. The term "imagination" has been used in various senses and it has been even classified academically into three distinct types by Kirkpatrick as follows:

"These are, first, reproductive imagination, in which the past is presented to the mind with the images arranged just as they were in the original experience; second, constructive imagination in which the separate images are combined not according to some particular experience but in accordance with their more usual arrangement or as directed by descriptions; third, creative

[17] W. H. Smyth, Is the inventive faculty a myth? Cassier's Magazine, 1897, 12, 676-683.

imagination in which the images are freely arranged in accordance with one's own feelings and purposes.

"The first type of imagination is quite similar to memory and may be identical with it. There may, however, be this difference; in memory we know that certain things happened at a particular time and place and in a certain order or relation, while in what is called reproductive imagination there may be less accuracy as to the order and relation of events but greater vividness of imagery, so that it almost seems as if the sensory experience were being repeated. It follows, therefore, that although reproductive imagination and memory are often nearly identical, yet there may be a high degree of imaginative activity with much inaccuracy of memory or a high degree of reliability of memory with a limited exercise of imagination.

"In constructive imagination laws of association and volition have a prominent part. The most common use of constructive imagination is that in which it is directed by words or symbols of some kind. . . .

"In creative imagination one pictures according to his emotions, desires, and purposes, although in doing so he is of course influenced by his previous mental habits. If you are asked to plan how the objects in a room of a certain size and description shall be arranged, for certain purposes or in order to produce the most beautiful effect, you must exercise your creative imagination. If you picture the room as quite similar to a particular model or with the arrangement most familiar, you employ less originality in creating the complex image than if the characteristics of various rooms are combined in such a way as to make one of a new type that is useful or beautiful. Freedom from the usual is one of the marked characteristics of creative imagination, yet if this freedom does not recognize the essential nature of things, the products of one's creative imagination may be neither useful nor beautiful. The inventor and the artist must show freedom in making new combinations, but the complex whole must be such as the nature of the material and the purpose of the creation demand, or it will be of no value." [18]

Kirkpatrick then concludes that imagination is a method of working. "There are three principal ways of meeting situations and of solving problems; one method is that of observing and manipulating objects, another, of imaging them, and the third is that of using symbols which represent them. . . .

"Imagination may therefore be regarded as a mental process in which images of things, persons, and events take the place of the sensations that may be or have been produced by them. It is also a mode of thinking in which images of experiences are the materials with which the mind works." [19]

Ribot in his "Essai sur l'imagination creatrice" recognizes that desire initiates the inventive process by spontaneously causing images which associate into groups by means of the imagination. He recognizes various kinds of imagination such as the esthetic, mathematical, musical, mystic, scientific, practical, mechanical and commercial. Ribot quotes with approval a letter of an engineer inventor which is here translated as follows: "The so-called creative imagination surely proceeds in very different ways according to temperament, aptitude, and, in the same individual following the mental disposition, the milieu. We may, however, as far as regards mechanical inventions, distinguish four sufficiently clear phases—the germ, incubation, flowering, and completion. By germ I mean the first idea coming to the mind to furnish a solution for a problem that the whole of one's observations, studies, and researches has put before one, or that, put by another, has struck one. Then comes incubation, often very long and painful, or again even unconscious. Instinctively as well as voluntarily one brings to the solution of the problem all the materials that the eyes and

---

[18] E. A. Kirkpatrick, Imagination and its place in education, New York, Ginn, 1920, 8-9.

[19] Ibid., 8-13.

ears can gather. When this latent work is sufficiently complete, the idea suddenly bursts forth. It may be at the end of a voluntary tension of mind, or on the occasion of a chance remark, tearing the veil that hides the surmised image. But this image always appears simple and clear. In order to get the ideal solution into practice, there is required a struggle against matter, and the bringing to an issue is the most thankless part of the inventor's work. In order to give consistence and body to the idea caught sight of enthusiastically in an aureole, one must have patience, a perseverance through all trials. One must view on all sides the mechanical agencies that should serve to set the image together, until the latter has attained the simplicity that alone makes invention possible. In this work of bringing the idea to a head, the same spirit of invention and imagination must be constantly drawn upon for the solution of all the details, and it is against this arduous requirement that the great majority of inventors rebel again and again. This is, then, I believe, how one may in a general way understand the genesis of an invention. It follows from this that here, as almost everywhere, the imagination acts through association of ideas. Thanks to a profound acquaintance with known mechanical methods, the inventor succeeds, through association of ideas, in getting novel combinations, producing new effects, towards the realization of which his mind has in advance been bent." [20]

The psychological theories of the causes of invention discussed in this chapter are exceedingly interesting. We have seen that no single theory can be accepted as a complete explanation of the complex process of invention. Invention is merely one phase of human behavior and we must await further advances in general psychology before any working theory for the inventive process can be formulated.

---

[20] T. Ribot, Essai sur l'imagination creatrice, Paris, Alcan, 1900, 222-223.

CHAPTER XIV

Training Inventors

THERE are schools and courses given for practically every field of human endeavor except inventing. We have schools for engineers, doctors, lawyers, artists, musicians, and hundreds of other professions and occupations but there are no schools for the inventor. Is it because invention cannot be taught? Music and the fine arts require a certain amount of native ability of the student in order that he may become really proficient. Assuming that inventing also requires certain traits and native ability why have no attempts been made to teach inventing in the schools? Must we depend on pure chance for our supply of inventors? Why should it not be possible to train people to invent? These questions are extremely interesting and of great social importance. Our entire civilization has been built up by the work of inventors and yet we have not developed a method of teaching the art of invention. The creative effort of inventors has given us our comfort, well-being and the progress of humanity but the methods of invention have hitherto been hardly studied.

"If the inclination to tinker and the ability to construct mechanical toys shows itself in a child, the parents are delighted and present the future Edison to every visitor with the pride of a collector who shows his gems. Thus the poor young genius will be filled with hopes and expectations that will make the disappointments, of which he will inevitably have his full share in his life, a heavier burden for him to bear. Strange to say, the enthusiasm over the child's dexterity lasts very seldom longer than childhood itself. Very few fathers and teachers are able to understand the importance of making those abilities the basis of the education of the child. Prejudice and custom and far more so, the necessity of earning money as soon as possible, prevent the boy from choosing his calling and sometimes the best part of a life is wasted before the man finds himself. If such a gifted boy had the opportunity of proper schooling to lay the foundation for an inventor's career, the world, perhaps, would rejoice over the progress he would help to bring about. But, as it is, many a man who was born to be an inventor, spends his life behind the counter, on the tailor's table or in the butcher shop." [1]

Before inventing can be taught an analysis must, of course, first be made of the actual methods employed by successful inventors. This has already been fully done in Chapter V.

In order to obtain the views of the inventors in regard to the possibility of teaching the art of inventing, the inventors of this study were asked the question "Can people be trained to invent?" Their replies are given in Table 18.

TABLE 18

CAN PEOPLE BE TRAINED TO INVENT?

	Number	Per cent
No, must have native ability	270	40.7
No	191	28.9
Yes	202	30.4
No answers	47	
Total	710	100.0

The great majority of the inventors did not believe that inventing could be taught and a large proportion of this group as seen from Table 18 believed in addition that it required native ability to invent. The general view expressed was that people can be trained to invent only in proportion as they have natural ability. The methods of work and the skill in analysis could be possibly improved by instruction.

[1] J. Reuter, Inventor's obstacles, The Inventor, 1910, 1, 11.

One inventor of this study, George R. Meyercord, made the following comments: "People can be trained to invent provided they have the creative mind lying dormant. Let me state that the mere placing of a boy in a research department, if he is by nature creative, springing ideas, asking questions, etc. will train him to invent. On the other hand, you might educate a person without that type of mind and try to develop his inventive ability without succeeding. My experience clearly demonstrates that you can cultivate a mind to follow through at a young age, provided the mechanical or research instinct is basically underlying the character of the person. In my experience I deal with four basic raw materials. My inventions are built around these products. I started out with one and gradually swung into others, and I definitely believe that the inventive mind that is good in one field is equally competent to step into other fields.

"The point I am trying to make is that I do not think it makes any difference if you transfer an inventor who has had contact with a research technical staff for years, to steel, iron, textiles or any other product, he will be competent to invent in any field, provided as stated, he is surrounded by technical men versed in the technique of that business. I have no doubt that a man thus trained if given a few months survey of the complaints and allowed to make a study of them, could direct his research staff very quickly along lines of improvement, because being a successful inventor in one field, he is bound to go back to the fundamentals very quickly and the reasons for being will very quickly disclose themselves to him.

"Young people may be roughly classed as (1) naturally inventive and (2) naturally non-inventive. The second class cannot be made inventive, whereas, members of the first class are likely to lose much of their inventiveness as the result of their environment, particularly the long experience in public school, high school and college. If one's youth has been characterized by originality, and if he has largely lost this characteristic as the result of his long training in acquiring standardized information, his inventiveness can be redeveloped by suitable experience. The ordinary engineer may follow standardized practice and never show inventive characteristics. To make successful devices the inventor appears to need three things: (1) inventiveness, (2) familiarity with the conditions under which his invention is to operate and (3) scientific principles employed in his device. It is not at all necessary that the inventor himself shall understand the scientific principles mentioned as the third requirement; this knowledge may be furnished by an associate who may not show inventiveness himself."

Another inventor, Mr. M. R. Wolfard, states that, "Invention requires an aptitude or attitude of mind which certainly not everyone possesses. Psychologically, it requires much the same special aptitude or adaptability which would be required by an artist, a musician, or a minister. You can train people to paint, to play, or to preach, and yet a real painter, a real musician or an inspiring minister seems to require something in the individual that is not necessarily a common attribute of all. It is exactly the same way with the inventor. Certainly there is a great deal of training which the inventor must give himself if he really attains any proficiency in the art of inventing, but unless he has some creative insight or aptitude for invention, he will never be really an inventor. There is, of course, one type of invention which many people might be trained to make if they found themselves in a favorable position. That is the type where a desired result is outlined possibly by someone else, and then they set to work merely by a process of experimental elimination of trying almost every conceivable thing which can be thought of to attain a result."

Some further interesting remarks in regard to training inventors were made by Mr. A. Y. Dodge, a very active inventor, as follows: "Personally, I believe that every person of more than an average intellect who possesses courage, self-confidence, optimism and imagination is an inventor in one form or another. The person who writes a novel is an inventor, so far as psychology is concerned. A housewife who creates a new dish is an inventor in like manner. Answering the question more directly, supplying that qualification which is absent, a person can be trained to invent. The quality and scope of an inventor depend a great deal on circumstances, environment, contacts made with others, resources for research work and resources for development work. An engineer might be a very good engineer for definite forms of work, who will confine himself very closely to precedent or to the written text yet possesses almost no inventive inclinations at all. It may be due to disheartenment or may be due to pessimism, for many engineers treat all new things pessimistically or possibly have never been drawn into work which demands of them to exercise originality.

"An inventor and nothing but an inventor need have very little technical knowledge, only sufficient for him to put two and two together to make a combination of two or more pieces of knowledge which may constitute an invention of a novel combination. Maybe his vision of this knowledge is a little broader or along a different slant than would ordinarily be the slant of the more conservative man. However, it is far more desirable that an inventor acquire considerable knowledge, particularly of a scientific type, if not of the technical type. It can be debated that technical knowledge has a tendency to dwarf originality. Personally, I don't think it should, if there is sufficient broad intellect in the personal make-up."

What kind of training should be given to one who shows inventive ability? A fairly comprehensive program has been suggested by Stratton: "Given a young man who has shown undoubted mechanical ingenuity, and keeping the past in mind, his training, commencing after his graduation from grammar school, should consist of the largest scope and opportunity for observing what has been done by others, rather than confinement to routine study. Mechanical drawing he should learn, but only sufficient to enable him to put his own ideas clearly upon paper and to read other drawings. If he is to become a professional inventor, he will not want to waste his time competing with skilled draftsmen. Models and drawings, and lectures thereupon, of every known description of mechanical movements should be provided, and every opportunity given for long and secluded study of the same. The drilling on this branch could not be too comprehensive or thorough. The calculation of the strength of beams and trusses, of the friction of the flow of liquids in pipes, would be wasted time. They are problems for the men of fixed theories and mathematical exactness—not for the imaginative inventor. A comprehensive study of patent laws and their application, and a familiarity with the method of searching for conflicting inventions, would be highly desirable. Lectures should be given upon the commercial view of inventing so that the young man may gain some insight into the methods of estimating the values of the problems he may be tempted to fix his mind upon. These lectures should also bear upon the formation and practice of stock companies and the adjustment and payment of royalties. The great purpose should be to impress upon the student the wisdom of always putting his efforts upon things which will pay; for in mechanical appliances it is really only those things which pay that are of real benefit. Easy access to manufactories of the greatest possible diversity would be one of the most essential requirements. Such practical demonstrations of machines and tools should be considered a part of the college course, and be made one of the greatest sources of information.

"Ample time and opportunity should be afforded for comprehensive study of trade magazines in every line of industry, for it is here more than in any other literature that the requirements of industry are revealed. Specializing of study would seem, in the light of the past, to be wasted time. You may keep a man's attention centered for months or even years on steam-engine construction, and if he is a true inventor he is likely, at any moment, to switch off to a labor-saving device in the show-making industry. His education and training should be confined to whatever will enable him to see and appreciate clearly difficulties in any existing apparatus in any line of manufacture, and should give him the confidence and patience to tackle that difficulty and eliminate it. Mechanical deftness is not an absolute necessity, although every opportunity should be afforded to qualify men in the use of tools and the making of their own models." [2]

Another scheme for the cultivation of invention has been given by William H. Smyth, inventor and engineer: "A rational system of education would be naturally divided into five or six loosely defined periods or stages.

"The first period should be devoted almost exclusively to observation and drawing representations of the things observed. The whole effort should be to acquire the habit of accuracy, and to discourage cursory observation and also to attain some skill in depicting simple objects.

"The second period should be an expansion of the previous one, both as to scope and detail, and should include exercises to cultivate clear visualization; also exercises which would increase the ability to recall all those things which naturally group around a given object.

"The third period, continuing and amplifying the foregoing manual training, should now assume a prominent place (though commenced earlier), and tools be introduced; also drawing involving precision and drawing tools, and exercises involving inference and simple analysis relating to concrete things, their form, material, structure and function. The physical organs of the senses, touch, taste, smell, hearing, seeing should all receive careful training with gradually increasing rigour, commencing in the previous periods. The faculties of judgment or comparison should be thoroughly cultivated

[2] G. F. Stratton, A college of invention, Scientific American, 1907, 97, 115.

by exercise in estimating size, number, weight, strength, etc., of things and material. Elementary science, simple arithmetic, reading and writing may be acquired in this period, but no particular emphasis need be placed upon the last two.

"In the fourth period, continuing the manual and sense training, physical geography, geometry, arithmetic may be emphasized so far as can be without the use of books, and derived from, and applied to, the objects concerned in the cultivation of manual skill. Exercises pertaining to concrete matters involving inference, elementary synthesis and analysis should receive particular attention. Books may be used sparingly during this period.

"In the fifth period, arithmetic, geometry, political geography, grammar, history, languages, and other studies involving abstract ideas and the use of books, may be introduced. Logical reasoning; problems involving unknown quantities; systematic training in contriving means for accomplishing definite ends and devising novel and useful construction, etc., should receive attention. To the end of the course, special emphasis should be placed upon the cultivation of logical reasoning with the direct object of cultivating individuality and personal initiative. Specialization may now be commenced very gradually and carefully.

"The sixth period should be devoted to learning a specific trade, art, profession, or calling in as specialized a manner as may be, and as nearly as possible under conditions of commercial necessity. The elements of time, cost, and utility should be given their proper consideration. At the completion of the education course every individual young man or young woman should be a productive member of society, competent of self-support, at least." [3]

There is no reason why it should not be possible to teach the art of inventing. In addition to the suggestions

[3] W. H. Smyth, Is the inventive faculty a myth? Cassier's Magazine, 1897, 12, 676-683.

just made the student should be made to study in detail the methods used by successful inventors. They should be given practical problems to solve and their methods of procedure should be carefully criticized by instructors who should be experienced inventors themselves. A study should be made of the important historical inventions and their evolution from crude beginnings. A study of the failures of inventors would be of great value. Unfortunately inventors never publish accounts of their failures but only of their successes. The exact accounts of the failures and mistakes of inventors would be of inestimable value. The reading of the biographies of eminent inventors would also be beneficial. Attention should be given to the influence of invention on economic life. The various industries should be studied from the standpoint of their inventions and the present-day problems and difficulties awaiting solution should be particularly stressed.

It is difficult to decide just what general education inventors should receive. No system of education can produce great inventors, artists, authors or composers. It has been found, however, that personal contact with great creators has been a powerful stimulus to many young men, and this is also true of inventors.

According to Iles: "While inventors owe their talents to nature, these talents need sound training, if at a master's hands, so much the better. Just as the best place to learn how to paint, is the studio of a great artist, so the best school for ingenuity is the workshop of a great inventor. Maudslay, who devised the slide-rest for lathes, and Clement who designed the first rotary planer, were trained by Bramah, who invented the famous hydraulic press, and locks of radically new and excellent pattern. Whitworth, who created lathes of new refinement, who established new and exact standards of measurement in manufacturing, was trained by Maudslay; so was Nasmyth, who devised the steam hammer. Mr. Edison in his laboratory and workshop has called forth the ingenuity of many an assistant who has since won fame and fortune by independent work."[4]

The question of education in general is full of difficulties and there have been many differences of opinion in regard to this subject, which have been far from fully settled. We can readily see that the education of the inventor would arouse still greater differences of opinion. Some believe that technical education thwarts the inventive powers and that formal education is a hindrance to originality. The argument advanced in favor of little education is that many of our great pioneer inventions have been made by men who had a very limited knowledge of the subject. If they knew of all the difficulties and failures of prior inventors they would have been completely discouraged from attempting the solution of the difficulty.

In view of the great increase of technical and scientific knowledge today an inventor could not proceed very far without a knowledge of at least the fundamental facts of his chosen field. Inventors of great ability have always been assiduous students, informing themselves of the necessary data by all possible means available. A thorough knowledge of scientific fundamentals without being too detailed would therefore be of great value to every inventor and this knowledge should be provided by a systematic method of instruction. An individual endowed with great inventive aptitude will probably invent no matter how little or how much formal education he may obtain but this aptitude will be made more efficient and effective by teaching and training.

[4] G. Iles, Inventors at work, New York, Doubleday, 1906, 299-300.

CHAPTER XV

The Psychology of Patent Law

PATENTS are granted by the Government through the Patent Office which passes upon the novelty of all inventions regularly presented to it for consideration. After the patent is issued it becomes a legal document which the owner can use for preventing all other persons from making, using or selling the invention, by bringing a suit against them in a Federal court. The issuance of the patent by the Patent Office constitutes a *prima facie* case for the owner of the patent as to its validity and novelty. The Patent Office has no power to withdraw a patent once it has been issued. However, the decision of the Patent Office is not final and in suits arising in the courts, the infringer has a right to set up as his defense the lack of novelty and originality of the patented invention. In such case the court must pass on the novelty of the patent and whether it really embraces a new invention.

The courts have been faced with some very difficult questions in determining the validity of a patent when the question of its novelty, originality or inventiveness is the deciding factor. This aspect of patent law will be discussed in this chapter.

The ultimate test of a patent is that it must be for a new and useful invention—such as a process, machine, composition of matter or article of manufacture, which have been defined in Chapter II. It is most interesting to observe that the courts determine the validity of a patent when the question of originality or novelty is concerned, not by referring to the invention itself, in the objective physical sense as it is apparent to us by our senses, but to the mental process by which it was evolved. This has been brought out by Walker in the standard treatise on patent law as follows: "To be a patentable invention there must be present a creative mental conception, as distinguished from the ordinary faculties of reasoning upon materials supplied by a special knowledge, and the facility of manipulation which results from its habitual and intelligent practice by those skilled in the art." [1]

According to Robinson, "Every invention contains two elements: (1) An idea conceived by the inventor; (2) an application of that idea to the production of a practical result. Neither of these elements is alone sufficient. An unapplied idea is not an invention. The application of an idea, not original with the person who applies it, is not an invention. Hence, the inventive act in reality consists of two acts: one mental, the conception of an idea; the other manual, the reduction of that idea to practice. It is especially in the mental act that the questions which confront us find their answer. . . .

"The mental faculties employed in the inventive act are the *creative* not the *imitative* faculties. An invention is the product of original thought. It involves the spontaneous conception of some idea not previously present to the mind of the inventor. Industry in exploring the discoveries and acquiring the ideas of others; wise judgment in selecting and combining them; mechanical skill in applying them to practical results; none of these are creation, none of these enter into the inventive act. Only when the mind of the inventor originates an idea new to himself, if not to all the world, does he call into exercise his own inventive skill, and perform the mental portion of the inventive act." [2]

The courts thus use the term invention not to signify the actual tangible invention but the concept underlying the physical invention. An invention is legally a mental operation and not a physical act. It is an idea expressed in physical form and not the material form itself. Ac-

[1] A. H. Walker, Patents, New York, Baker, Voorhis & Co., 1929, 6th edition, 67.

[2] W. C. Robinson, Treatise on the law of patents, Boston, Little, Brown & Co., 1890, Vol. I, 116-120.

cording to Waite: "Of first importance is the proposition that an invention is not tangible. It is a concept; a thing evolved by mind. It is not a tangible thing produced by manual effort. The act of invention is undeniedly and undeniably a mental and not a manual act." [3]

The test used by the courts is that the invention requires a mental act, a new idea as well as a new physical form. "A concept of anything to be given tangible form by man, is so far as its subject-matter is concerned, patentable." [4] However, not every idea is patentable, for a patentable invention must be confined to the limited field defined by the legal statutes.

It is interesting to note that the courts are not concerned with the time element involved in invention. They fully recognize that the inventive process cannot be consciously controlled. Thus Judge Wheeler said: "An invention is not like a will, depending on intention. It is a fact, and, if the fact exists, it does not appear to be material whether it came by design, or accidentally without being bidden." [5]

According to Robinson: "The law draws no distinction between those operations of the creative faculties which manifest themselves in long-continued study and experiment, and those which reach their end by sudden intuition or apparent accident. Here also is a region in which human knowledge is at fault. Indeed, it may well be doubted whether the creative act is ever otherwise than instantaneous and intuitive, and whether research and reflection ever do more than clear the way for, and dispose the mind toward those sudden apprehensions of the truth to which in literature and the arts we give the names 'invention' and 'discovery.' The law does not attempt to settle questions which thus lie beyond the reach of mental science. Wherever the creative faculties have evidently been at work, it inquires neither as to the

[3] J. B. Waite, Patent law, Princeton, Princeton Univ. Press, 1920, 24.

[4] Ibid., 26.

[5] Aniline & Cochrane, 1879, 16 Blatch, 155, 160.

method nor the duration of their exercise. The patient labors of a life-time, the unpremeditated flash of an original thought upon the mind, the revelation made to an appreciative intellect by some trivial accident, all stand upon an equal footing both in character and merit, and are entitled to the same reward." [6]

The mental part of the inventive act is finally analyzed by Robinson to be "an exercise of the creative faculties, generating an idea which is clearly recognized and comprehended by the inventor, and is both complete in itself and capable of application to a practical result. . . . Two ideas are present to the mind of an inventor during his performance of the inventive act: (1) The idea of an end to be accomplished; (2) the idea of a means by which that end can be attained. . . . That rule excludes from the inventive act every mental operation which does not involve the exercise of the creative faculties. The application of this rule will demonstrate that the idea of means alone, and not the idea of end, is the result of the inventive act, and, therefore, is the essence of the invention. . . . The end to be accomplished by the invention is the satisfaction of a public want. This want is an existing fact. It grows inevitably out of the relations which man occupies to the external world. It can be satisfied only by such a change in those relations as will supply or terminate the want. . . . It is thus evident that the conception of an idea of means by an inventor includes two mental processes: a process of discovery, and a process of construction. The process of discovery consists in the finding out, by his own endeavors, of those qualities in the force, the object, or the mode of application, which render their union possible. The process of construction consists in combining the three factors into the idea conceived. Without the former process, the latter would demand no exercise of the inventive faculties. Without the latter, the former would result only in an addition to the

[6] W. C. Robinson, Treatise on law of patents, Boston, Little, Brown & Co., 1890, Vol. I, 126-127.

inventor's knowledge of the properties of things, and not in the production of new operative means. Taken together they constitute the complete mental part of the inventive act, creating a new and original idea of means which requires only reduction to practice to make it useful in the arts." [7]

How do the courts determine the mental operation of the inventor? The method used is highly interesting psychologically. The evidence presented to the court determines whether or not the mental part of the inventive act has been performed. The court does not look into the actual operations which have taken place in the mind of the inventor but it rather pursues an abstruse ideal method somewhat as follows: It begins with an ideal problem confronting the ideal inventor. He is assumed to have all the knowledge and experience which an ideal worker in his field is supposed to possess. The courts designate this worker as a "person skilled in the art." Ideal experiments are then imagined by the court to be attempted by the inventor and the court may conclude that true invention is present if the results from the old to the new have apparently been made by a leap of the imagination or by the exercise of "inventive faculty," "creative genius" or "ingenuity" which could not possibly be foreseen or made by a person skilled in the art. Invention by legal definition is thus the process of mind which creates and "it is the giving birth to a new idea capable of physical embodiment." [8]

The patentability of an inventor can only be determined by deciding whether it required a creative mental process to make an addition to the common stock of ideas and not the mere logical development of known ideas which a person of ordinary skill and knowledge in a given field can accomplish. In other words, ordinary reasoning, inference or deduction is not invention in patent law.

[7] W. C. Robinson, Treatise on law of patents, Boston, Little, Brown & Co., 1890, Vol. I, 132-143.

[8] H. C. Merwin, Patentability of invention, Boston, Little, Brown & Co., 1883, 10.

In this connection we quote Merwin: "Invention is imagination; it is the very opposite of reasoning or inference; it is a single act of the mind; rather an instantaneous operation than a process. It has no stages; the essence of it is that it dispenses with them.

"In the process of reasoning or inference the conclusion is reached both gradually and inevitably. The mind is led on from one point to another, until it reaches a conclusion from which there is no escape. Whereas, when the mind invents, it starts with the conclusion. The conclusion flashes, so to say, upon the mind. The conclusion, therefore, either carries conviction with it, or it has to be verified; for the mind does not perceive how it has been reached.

"In every case the truth revealed by invention can be verified by reason; for this is but to say that nothing happens without a cause, and when, by an act of invention, a certain truth has been reached, the mind can work backward, as it were, and analyze the causes (reasons) upon which depends the existence of the material thing invented.

"But reason would never lead one to the truths and ideas which are the objects of invention; in fact, most often it leads directly away from them. And it is for this reason that invention is so difficult and comparatively so rare. It is not a sort of elevated reason; it is a faculty which differs in kind from reason, which often, in truth, is free to act only when reason has been thrust aside, and its conclusions ignored, nay, denied. Invention, then, is in the nature of a guess. The mind leaps across a logical chasm. Instead of working out a conclusion, it imagines it." [9]

The same ideas have been repeatedly expressed by the courts and they are generally accepted as basic principles in patent law.

[9] H. C. Merwin, Patentability of invention, Boston, Little, Brown & Co., 1883, 22.

A moment's reflection will show that "the leap across a logical chasm" is nothing else but the formulation of a successful solution accomplished by the neural activity initiated in the inventor after he has felt a want and seeks to satisfy it, as explained in Chapter VI. If the judge follows out in his mind the mental processes of an ideal inventor and believes that what he has accomplished is beyond ordinary expectation and reasoning he will say that the inventor has exercised his "inventive faculty" and should be accordingly rewarded.

Although Merwin states that invention is imagination he admits that reasoning may enter in invention, especially where a long course of thought and labor are involved. "In such case the inventor may be supplemented by a process of reasoning, the inventive idea furnishing the starting-point for such a process. And the value of the improvement finally reached may depend upon this development of the inventive thought, but the original conception, not the working out thereof, is the gist of the improvement and makes it patentable. This shows very clearly the difference between reasoning and invention. In a process of reasoning every step is not only valuable, but necessary; each step is an advance; each step brings us nearer to the conclusion, and at last the conclusion follows inevitably. It was latent, so to say, in the premises, and needed but a process of reasoning to evoke it. Hence it was within the reach of all men capable of conducting the ordinary process of reasoning. But the thought or experiments which precede an invention are only gropings in the dark. However accumulated, they prove nothing, and they do not necessarily lead to anything. The inventive thought does not depend upon them, and cannot be verified by them. In a certain sense they may have been necessary; they may have cleared the ground, prepared the way for the arrival of the inventive thought; in fact, they may have rendered its arrival possible. Nevertheless, they have not caused its arrival. Reasoning is unravelling, and invention weaving, of thought. Reasoning is an analytic, invention, a synthetic process. In one case a truth is drawn out; in the other it is constructed." [10]

We have seen in Chapter V the importance of reasoning in inventing, for after a solution is formulated a careful analysis must be made of all the factors suggested by the solution.

We can readily appreciate that the personal element of a judge may affect the decision to a very great extent depending on his individual intelligence and knowledge. He may not follow the ideal inventor's mental process carefully or he may not appreciate all the difficulties involved. He may also be unable to go back mentally to the condition of the art which existed before the invention which he has to decide upon has been made. Some inventions are so simple that once they are made they appear to be obvious although it occurred to no one before for many years.

Unfortunately we do not have a central court devoted only to patent litigation so that quite often the judges have no technical knowledge whatsoever and they have great difficulty in appreciating the achievement or lack of achievement of the inventor. This state of affairs has resulted in many conflicting decisions, as we might expect.

The hope of measuring invention by a psychological group test would thus naturally arise. A practical method of accomplishing this result would be of great value because the problem of determining whether invention is present is continually arising in the Patent Office as well as in the courts. We have already seen the difficulty in defining invention. We can only define it by what it is not. The personal element in deciding whether invention exists is very great. It would, therefore, be very dangerous to have the opinion of one individual decide the question since he might be influenced by factors which should have no weight given to them.

---

[10] H. C. Merwin, Patentability of invention, Boston, Little, Brown & Co., 27.

In most patent cases the judge who is called upon to decide the validity of a patent knows at the outset of the trial practically nothing that a person skilled in the particular art should know. However, by means of counsel and expert witnesses he finally becomes familiar with the state of the art so as to be able to render his decision. It should, therefore, be possible to educate a fairly intelligent group, such as a college group, by the same process so that in presenting any problem to them the personal factor in evaluating the inventive element would be eliminated.

The purpose of a psychological test [12] given by me in 1927 was to determine whether this was possible.

In order to reduce the energy and time in educating the group in the prior art twenty of the simplest type of adjudicated cases were selected which involved substitution of material. The court decisions as well as the patents were first studied carefully with a view to present to the group very clearly what was old and what was new. One example might be useful to give here. Brown v. D. C. 130 U. S. 87 was presented substantially as follows:

"Stone blocks having a single plain surface and inclined sides are old. Wooden blocks are made for the first time having a similar shape so that when laid on their longer ends, wedged shaped grooves are formed to be filled with cement or similar material. It is claimed that the filling adheres better to wooden blocks than to the stone ones, because they are softer and will indent. Is there any invention in making wooden blocks like the stone ones?"

All the other cases were similarly presented to a college class in psychology at George Washington University, the group consisting of 48 members. The aim was to give to the class an unbiased and clear grasp of the essential facts of the problem very much in the same way as it was presented to the Court. The group was then asked

[12] J. Rossman, A psychological test for invention, Journal of the Patent Office Society, 1927, 9, 348-356.

to write yes or no as their answer and give one line for their reason. In this way it was hoped to obtain experimental determination of the following:

First of all, assuming that the decision of the Court was correct for the given problem, it would be interesting to see what the average person would think of the same question. The class did not have any patent experience nor was it instructed in any matter concerning invention or the rules followed by the courts in cases involving substitution of material. They were asked to decide according to their own opinion and ideas of invention in each particular case.

Secondly, it was hoped that if a sharp differentiation were obtained by the group as a whole then it would be possible to determine the inventive element existing in a patent by a group test so as to determine one of the factors of its validity.

The test shows very clearly that in spite of the fact that it is very difficult to define invention, the average college group has a very definite conception of invention which agrees very remarkably with the views of the Court, at least it can be said for the present, in cases involving substitution of material. In the cases of non-invention, however, the group had much more difficulty in deciding the question of non-invention, the average agreement being much lower than in the cases involving invention. The group, in other words, was quicker to discern invention from non-invention. The test also shows that it is possible to use a group test to determine whether invention is present or not in a given case by eliminating the very troublesome factor introduced by the personal element.

In conclusion, we find that one of the established principles in patent law is that an invention is an unchanging fact to which the law must conform. Our present patent laws and court decisions have so far been serious though empirical attempts to conform to the all important psychological factors which underly invention.

Selected Bibliography

ARTICLES

Anon., Accidental discoveries, Mechanical Engineering, 1926, 48, 865-866.

Anon., Fortuitous discovery, Scientific American Supplement, 1898, 46, 19016.

Anon., Dr. Georges Claude discusses invention, Scientific American, June 1929, 568-569.

Anon., Inventors too cautious, Scientific American, 1915, 113, 106.

Anon., Men of wealth as inventors, Scientific American, 1902, 86, 270-271.

Anon., Necessity and invention, Scientific American, 1911, 105, 22.

Anon., The qualities an inventor must possess, Scientific American, 1902, 86, 242.

Anon., Some accidental inventions, Public Opinion, 1898, 25, 88-89.

Babson, R. W. Twenty ways to make a million, The Forum, May 1929, 277-281.

Bache, R. Some modern inventions which are ancient history, Scientific American, 1907, 96, 44.

Baker, J. B. The modern profession of inventing, American Machinist, 1910, 33, 467-469.

Baxter, W. Forecasting the progress of invention, Popular Science Monthly, 1897, 51, 307-314.

Bell, A. G. Discovery and invention, National Geographic Magazine, 1914, 25, 649-655.

—— Prizes for the inventor, National Geographic Magazine, 1917, 31, 131-146.

Bellet, D. Le role de l'invention dans la vie sociale, Revue des Sciences politiques, Paris, 1917, 38, 472-481.

Bernard, L. L. Invention and social progress, American Journal of Sociology, 1923, 29, 1-33.

Brimhall, D. R. Family resmeblances among American men of science, American Naturalist, 1922, 56, 504-547; 1923, 57, 74-88, 137-152, 326-344.

Carr, L. J. A study of 137 typical inventors, American Sociological Society, 1929, 33, 204-206.

Cattell, J. M. A statistical study of eminent men, Popular Science Monthly, 1903, 62, 359-377.

—— A statistical study of American men of science, Science, 1906, N. S. 24, 732-744.

Charnock, G. F. Some fallacies concerning invention, Institution of Mechanical Engineers, 1926, 1, 35-36.

Claudy, C. H. Captive inventor, Illustrated World, 1917, 26, 716, 721.

Clerk, D. Discovery and invention, Journal of Royal Society of Arts, 1917, 66, 50-61.

Cooley, C. H. Genius, Fame and the comparison of races, Annals of Political and Social Science, 1897, 9, 317-358.

Coryton, J. Accidental inventions, Macmillan, 1861, 4, 75-85.

Davies, G. R. A statistical study on the influence of the environment, Quarterly Journal University of North Dakota, April, 1924.

Decharme, C. Le hasard, et l'imprevu dans les decouvertes et les recherches scientifiques, La Lumière Electrique (Paris), 1892, 45, 439-446, 490-496, 592-596.

Del Mar, A. Inventions of ancient Rome, Scientific American, 1905, 93, 135.

Dexter, E. S. Relation between occupation of parents and intelligence of school children, School and Society, 1923, 17, 612-616.

Draper, G. O. Inventors and their peculiarities, Textile World, 1925, 67, 1662.

Dudeney, H. E. Antiquity of modern inventions, Strand, 1913, 45, 446-450.

Duff, J. F. and Thomson, G. H. The social and geographical distribution of intelligence in Northumberland, British Journal of Psychology, Gen. Sec., 1923, 14, 192-198.

Du Puy, Wm. A. A professional inventor, Scientific American, 1912, 106, 292-293.

Ellis, G. B. Luck or chance in invention, Transactions of Chartered Institute of Patent Agents, 1916, 34, 102-109.

Epstein, R. C. Industrial invention: heroic or systematic? The Quarterly Journal of Economics, 1926, 40, 232-272.

Fairchild, D. and Hart, H. A million years of evolution in tools, Scienific Monthly, 1929, 28, 71-79.

Feldhaus, F. M. Old inventions, Scientific American Supplement, 1906, 61, 25188-25189.

Field, C. Mechanical invention as a form of expression, Mechanical Engineering, 1928, 50, 447-453.

Fryer, D. Occupation—intelligence standards, School and Society, 1922, 16, 273-277.

Gaisman, J. The autographic kodak, Scientific American, 1914, 111, 101.

Gammeter, J. R. We make inventing an everyday job, System 1925, 47, 181-183.

Gilfillan, S. C. Who invented it? Scientific Monthly, 1927, 25, 529-534.

—— Invention in the history of the ship, American Sociological Society, 1929, 23, 200-203.

Gillette, H. P. Why inventions and discoveries of natural laws are often made by amateurs, Engineering and Contracting, 1926, 65, 219-220.

Greenawalt, W. and Greenawalt, K. W. A plea for a U. S. Court of patent appeals, Mining and Metallurgy, 1930, 11, 85-90,

Grosvenor, W. M. The seeds of progress, Chemical Markets, 1929, 24, 23-26.

Gruenberg, A. Channels great minds run in, Forum, 1910, 43, 540-549.

Haines, T. H. Cross breeding of ideas as a factor in invention, Mental Hygiene, 1922, 6, 83-92.

Harris, D. F. Living mechanisms before inventions, Dalhousie Review, 1921, 1, 47-57.

Harrison, H. S. Analysis and factors of invention, Man, 1927, 27, 43-47.

—— Inventions abstrusive, directional, and independent, Man, 1926, 26, 117-121.

—— Variations and imitations in invention, Man, 1926, 26, 154-158.

Hart, H. Preliminary conclusions from a study of inventors, American Sociological Society, 1927, 21, 191-194.

Henderson, J. B. Invention as a link in scientific and economic progress, Scientific Monthly, 1927, 25, 347-361.

Higbee, F. G. Invention, research and teaching, American Machinist, 1913, 38, 240-241.

Horwill, H. W. The parentage of invention, Discovery, 1921, 2, 212-214.

Hrdlicka, A. Race deterioration and destruction with special reference to the American people, 1928, Proceedings of the Third Race Betterment Conference.

—— Man's future in the light of his past and present, Proceedings American Philosophical Society, 1929, 68, No. 1.

Iles, G. Why progress is by leaps and bounds, Popular Science Monthly, 1896, 49, 216-230.

Jefferson, M. The geographic distribution of inventiveness, Geographical Review, 1929, 19, 649-661.

Jenkins, C. F. Rewarding the inventor, Scientific American, 1913, 109, 227.

Joy, B. Invention and the inventor, Gas Journal, 1924, 168, 38-39.

Kaempffert, W. Systematic invention, Forum, 70, 2010-2018.

Kelly, F. C. How inventions are made, Munsey, 1919, 66, 29-39.

Kettering, C. F. Hurdles to jump for inventors, Popular Mechanics, 1929, 52, 954-959.

Kirkegaard, G. Inventors and curious inventions, Cassier's, 1904, 26, 396.

Kroeber, A. L. The Eskimos as aboriginal inventors, Scientific American, 1914, 110, 54.

Leicester, A. The early life of great inventors, Engineering Magazine, 1894, 7, 639-645.

Lincoln, Abraham. Discoveries and inventions, Journal of the Patent Office Society, 1928, 10, 314-320.

Lowy, J. The nature of invention, Scientific American Supplement, 1911, 71, 322.

Mach, E. On the part played by accident in invention and discovery, Monist, 1896, 6, 161-175.

—— Inventors I have met, Monist, 1912, 22, 230-242.

Marconi, G. Every man his own inventor, Colliers, 1922, 70, 5-6.

Mason, O. T. Traps of the American Indians, Annual Report of Smithsonian Institution, 1901, 461-473.

Mitman, C. W. Watchmakers and inventors, Scientific Monthly, 1927, 25, 58-64.

Mills, F. How inventors invent, Illustrated World, 1916, 25, 241-243.

Moffett, F. J. Imagination in engineering, Journal of the Institution of Electrical Engineers, 1925, 64, 11-15.

Nearing, S. The geographical distribution of American genius? Popular Science Monthly, 1914, 85, 189-199.

—— The younger generation of American genius, Scientific Monthly, 1916, 2, 48-61.

Ogburn, W. and Thomas D. Are inventions inevitable? Political Science Quarterly, 1922, 37, 83-98.

Ogburn, W. F. Inventions and discoveries, American Journal of Sociology, 1928, 34, 25-39.
Ogden, C. K. Bentham on invention, Psyche, 1929, Oct. 102-109.
Ostwald, W. The art of discovery, Scientific American Supplement, 1910, 70, 123-124.
—— Systematisches Erfinden, Prometheus, 1912, 24, 5-8, 17-21.
Palmer, W. K. The inventive faculty, Education, 1899, 18, 372-374.
Penkert, W. Psychologie des Erfindens, Die Umschau, 1922, 26, 151-153.
Pentz, A. D. How an invention is made, Engineering Magazine, 1892, 3, 96-103.
Pestel, A. The development of inventions, Cassier's Magazine, 1910, 38, 75-78.
Pressey, S. L. and Ralston, R. The relation of the general intelligence of school children to the occupation of their fathers, Journal of Educational Psychology, 1919, 3, 366-373.
Prindle, E. J. The art of inventing, Proceedings of the American Institute of Electrical Engineers, 1906, 25, No. 7.
Reeves, T. A. An inventor's fantasy, Scientific American, 1905, 93, 422.
Reuter, J. Inventor's obstacles, The Inventor, 1910, 1, 11.
Rossman, J. A psychological test for invention, Journal of the Patent Office Society, 1927, 9, 348-356.
—— The relation of intelligence to invention, Journal of the Patent Office Society, 1927, 9, 511-534, 565-571.
—— Abraham Lincoln the inventor, Journal of the Patent Office Society, 1928, 10, 292-296.
—— The correlation of intelligence and invention, Journal of the Patent Office Society, 1928, 10, 356-359.
—— Seasonal variations in applying for and granting patents, Journal of the Patent Office Society, 1929, 11, 99-103.
—— The obstacles and pitfalls of inventors, Journal of the Patent Office Society, 1930, 12, 195-217.
—— Heredity and invention, Journal of Heredity, 1930, 21, 507-512.
—— Mutiple invention, Journal of the Patent Office Society, 1930, 12, 507-516.
—— The negro inventor, Journal of the Patent Office Society, 1930, 12, 549-553.
—— War and invention, American Journal of Sociology, 1931, 36, 625-633.
—— The motives of inventors, Quarterly Journal of Economics, 1931, 45, 522-528.
—— Engineers as inventors, Journal of the Patent Office Society, 1931, 13, 376-383.
Royce, J. The psychology of invention, Psychological Review, 1898, 5, 113-144.
Sargeret, J. Apprendre à inventer, Psychologie et vie, 1927, 1, No. 9, 8-10.
Seely, F. A. The genesis of inventions, Transactions of Anthropological Society, 1885, 3.
Seillière, E. Bewusstes und Unbewusstes im Erfindergenie, Internationale Monatschrift für Wissenschaft, Kunst und Technik, 1911-12, 6, 33-46.
Severance, B. Bibliography on inventions, Libraries, 1928, 33, 247-250.

Smith, E. H. The criminal as an inventor, Scientific American, 1924, 130, 376-377, 426.

Smith, L. W. The inventor and his reward, Scientific American, 1913, 108, 31.

Smyth, W. H. Is the inventive faculty a myth? Cassier's Magazine, 1897, 12, 676-683.

—— Practical inventing, Cassier's Magazine, 1900, 18, 117-128.

—— The tool, the machine, the man, Cassier's Magazine, 1901, 20, 379-387.

Stratton, G. F. A college of invention, Scientific American, 1907, 97, 115.

—— The pursuit of inventing as a business, Engineering Magazine, 1907, 33, 408-412.

Strother, F. Modern profession of inventing, World's Work, 1905, 10, 6289.

Suplee, H. H. The professional mechanical inventor, Engineering Magazine, 1894, 8, 842-848.

—— The principle of reversal, Scientific American, 1913, 109, 344.

Tanner, A. E. Certain social aspects of invention, American Journal of Psychology, 1915, 26, 388-416.

Tennant, A. Inventive activity, sedatives and stimulants, Transactions of the Chartered Institute of Patent Agents, 1927, 46, 20-37.

Terrell, C. The psychology of invention, Chartered Institute of Patent Agents, 1910, 29, 25-44.

Thompson, E. P. An analytical and systematic method of inventing, The Electrical World, 1184, 4, 208.

Ulm, A. H. A rich man's son who has made more than 200 inventions, Forbes, 1924, 14, 483-484.

Warner, E. P. The nature of invention, The Harvard Graduates Magazine, 1923, 31, 310-317.

Westinghouse, G. How I invented the air brake, Scientific American, 1911, 104, 602-603, 627, Vol. 105, 13, 34.

Winkler, O. Ueber die geistigen Vorgange beim Konstruieren und Erfinden, Motorwagon, 1921, 26, 534-538.

Woodworth, R. S. The mechanism of progress, Scientific American Supplement, 1910, 69, 279.

Wright, M. Inventors who have achieved commercial success, Scientific American, 1927, Vol. 136: 17, 105, 176, 249, 327, 396. 1927, Vol. 137: 33-35, 140-142, 242-243, 328, 329, 414, 415, 513-515. 1928, Vol. 138: 28-29, 134-135, 320-321.

Wyman, W. I. Age of production in invention and other fields, Journal of the Patent Office Society, 1918, 439-447.

—— Patents for scientific discoveries, Journal of the Patent Office Society, 1929, 11, 533-557.

BOOKS

Allport, F. H. Social psychology, Boston, Houghton Mifflin, 1924.
Annual Reports of the Commissioner of Patents, Wash., D. C., Gov't Printing Office, 1836-1929.
Anon., Great inventors, London, Ward & Lock, 1864.
Arnold, F. Psychology of association, New York, Science Press, 1906.
Avram, M. H. Patenting and promoting inventions, New York, McBride, 1918.
Baff, Wm. E. Inventions, New York, Van Nostrand, 1920.
Bakewell, F. C. Great facts, London, Houlston & Wright, 1858.
Baldwin, J. M. Social and ethical interpretations in mental development, New York, Macmillan, 1897.
Barlow, C. How to make money by patents, London, Marlborough, 1879.
Barnes, H. E. Living in the twentieth century, Indianapolis, Bobbs-Merrill, 1928.
Beach, W. G. An introduction to sociology and social problems, New York, Houghton Mifflin, 1925.
Beard, C. A. Toward civilization, New York, Longman, Green & Co., 1930.
Bernard, L. L. An introduction to social psychology, New York, Holt, 1926.
Bogardus, E. S. Essentials of social psychology, Los Angeles, J. R. Miller, 1923.
—— Fundamentals of social psychology, New York, Century, 1924.
Bowden, W. The industrial revolution, New York, F. S. Crofts, 1928.
Breese, B. B. Psychology, New York, Scribner, 1917.
Brigham, C. C. A study of American intelligence, Princeton, Princeton Univ. Press, 1922.
Burnley, J. The romance of invention, London, Cassell, 1892.
Byrn, E. The progress of invention, New York, Munn, 1900.
Carr, H. A. Psychology, a study of mental activity, New York, Longmans, 1926.
Carter, T. F. The invention of printing in China, New York, Columbia Univ. Press, 1925.
Cattell, J. M. American men of science, Garrison Science Press, 1910, 1921, 1927, 2nd, 3rd, 4th edition.
Chase, S. Men and Machines, New York, Macmillan, 1929.
Claremont, C. A. Intelligence and mental growth, New York, Norton, 1928.
Clark, S. E. Learn to invent, practical instruction and valuable suggestions, S. E. Clark, Phila., 1907.
Collins, A. F. A bird's eye view of invention, New York, Crowell, 1926.
Cox, J. W. Mechanical aptitude, London, Methuen, 1928.
Darrow, F. L. Masters of science and invention, New York, Harcourt, 1923.
Davenport, N. Essay on inventions, 1881.
Delaney, M. G. The inventor's manual of valuable information, New York, G. E. Perry, 1919.
Dewey, J. How we think, New York, Heath, 1910.
Dickinson, Z. C. Economic motives, Cambridge, Harvard Univ. Press, 1922.

Dircks, H. Perpetuum mobile, London, Spon, 1870.
Doolittle, W. H. Inventions in the century, London, W. & R. Chambers, 1903.
Dorland, W. A. N. The age of mental virility, New York, Century, 1908.
Dow, G. S. Society and its problems, New York, Crowell, 1922.
Dresser, H. W. Psychology in theory and application, New York, Crowell, 1924.
Dumas, G. Traitè de psychologie, Paris, Alcan, Vol. II, 426-476, 1924.
Edman, I. Human traits, Boston, Houghton Mifflin, 1920.
Ellis, Havelock. A study of British genius, London, Hurst and Blackett, 1904, rev. ed., 1926.
Ellis, R. S. The psychology of individual differences, New York, Appleton, 1928.
Ellwood, C. A. Sociology and modern problems, New York, American Book Co., 1913.
—— An introduction to social psychology, New York, Appleton, 1917.
—— Sociology in its psychological aspects, New York, Appleton, 1921.
—— The psychology of human society, New York, Appleton, 1925.
—— Cultural evolution, New York, Century, 1927.
Engelmeyer, P. K. V. Der Dreiakt als Lehre von der Technik und der Erfindung, Berlin, Heymann, 1910.
Engineering foundation, Popular Research narratives, Baltimore, Williams & Wilkins, 1924.
Fessenden, R. A. The deluged civilization, Boston, T. J. Russell Print, 1923.
Fiske, B. A. Invention the master-key to progress, New York, Dutton, 1921.
Folsom, J. K. Culture and social progress, New York, Longmans, 1928.
Forman, S. E. Stories of useful inventions, New York, Century, 1911.
Fournier, E. Le vieux-neuf, Paris, E. Dentu, 1877.
Freyd, M. Personalities of the socially and mechanically inclined. Psychological Monographs, Vol. 33, No. 4, 1924.
Fuller, B. F. Man as he is, London, J. Murray, 1916.
Galton, F. Hereditary genius, New York, Appleton, 1869, reprint, 1914.
General information concerning patents, Wash., D. C., U. S. Gov't Printing Office, 1927.
Giddings, F. H. Principles of sociology, New York, Macmillan, 1916.
Glascock, E. S. Manual of patent office procedure, Federalsburg, Md., J. W. Stowell, 1929.
Goddard, H. H. Psychology of the normal and subnormal, New York, Dodd-Mead, 1919.
Goldenweiser, A. A. Early civilization, New York, Knopf, 1922.
Gore, G. Art of discovery, London, Longmans, 1878.
—— The scientific basis of national progress, London, Williams & Norgate, 1882.
Gregory, R. A. Discovery the spirit and service of science, New York, Macmillan, 1918.
Hale, E. E. Stories of invention, Boston, Roberts Bros., 1885.

Hargreaves, H. L. The faculty of imagination, London, Cambridge Univ. Press, 1927.
Hart, H. The science of social relations, New York, Holt, 1927.
Hart, J. B. The mechanical investigations of Leonardo da Vinci, Chicago, Open court, 1925.
Hearings held before the committee of patents, Wash., D. C., Gov't Printing Office, 1919.
Hearn, W. E. Plutology, London, Macmillan, 1864.
Herrick, C. J. Brains of rats and men, Chicago, Univ. of Chicago Press, 1926.
Hirsch, N. D. M. A study of natio-racial mental differences, Worcester, Clark Univ., 1926.
Holland, M. Industrial explorers, New York, Harper, 1928.
Hollingworth, H. L. Psychology, its facts and principles, New York, Appleton, 1928.
Hopkins, G. M. Inventor's manual, New York, Norman W. Henley, 1924.
Hopkins, N. M. The outlook for research and invention, New York, Van Nostrand, 1919.
Howe, H. Memoirs of the most eminent American mechanics, New York, Harper, 1847.
Howson, H. Patents and the useful arts, Phila., Times Printing House, 1878.
Hubert, P. Inventors, New York, Scribner, 1893.
Iles, G. Flame electricity and the camera, New York, Doubleday, 1901.
—— Inventors at work, New York, Doubleday, 1906.
—— Leading American inventors, New York, Holt, 1912.
Jacobus, A. B. Developing new inventions, Kansas City, Mo., Press of Franklin Hudson Pub. Co., 1905.
Judd, C. H. The psychology of social institutions, New York, Macmillan, 1927.
Kaempffert, W. A popular history of American invention, New York, Scribner, 2 vols., 1924.
Kelsey, C. The physical basis of society, New York, Appleton, 1916.
Kirkpatrick, E. A. Imagination and its place in education, New York, Ginn, 1920.
Knowlson, T. S. Originality, New York, Lippincott, 1918.
Kohler, W. Gestalt psychology, New York, Liveright, 1929.
Kroeber, A. L. Anthropology, New York, Harcourt, 1923.
Linley, C. M. Practical advice to inventors and patentees, London, Pitman, 1925.
Lundberg, G. A. et al. Trends in American sociology, New York, Harper, 1929.
Macomber, Wm. Engineers handbook on patents, Boston, Little, Brown, 1913.
McFarlane, M. A study of practical ability, London, Cambridge Univ. Press, 1925.
Marot, H. Creative impulse in industry, New York, Dutton, 1918.
Mason, O. T. The Origin of invention, London, W. Scott, 1895.
Merwin, H. C. Patentability of invention, Boston, Little, Brown & Co., 1883.
Neuburger, A. Erfinder and Erfindungen, Berlin, Ullstein, & Co., 1913.
—— The technical arts of the ancients, New York, Macmillan, 1930.

Ogburn, Wm. F. Social change, New York, Huebsch, 1922.
Ogden, C. K. The meaning of psychology, New York, Harper, 1926.
Ostwald, W. Erfinder und Entdecker, Die Gesellschaft Smml. Sorzial psychol. Monograph 24, Frankfort, 1908.
Patrick, G. T. W. The psychology of social reconstruction, New York, Houghton Mifflin, 1920.
Paulhan, F. Psychologie de l'invention, Paris, Alcan, 1901.
Payntner, R. H., Jr. A psychological study of trade-mark infringement, New York, Columbia Univ. Archives of Psychology, No. 42, 1920.
Phin, J. The seven follies of science, New York, Van Nostrand, 1912.
Pintner, R. Intelligence testing, New York, Holt, 1923.
Potts, H. E. Patents, invention and method, London, Open Court, 1924.
Ravenshear, A. F. The industrial and commercial influence of the English patent system, London, T. F. Unwin, 1908.
Raymond, W. C. Curiosities of the U. S. patent office, Syracuse, Wm. C. Raymond, 1888.
Ribot, T. Essai sur l'imagination creatrice, Paris, Alcan, 1900.
Roberts, G. L. Patentability of inventions, Boston, Little, Brown, 1927, 2 vols.
Robinson, H. Inventors and inventions, New York, H. Robinson, 1911.
Robinson, Wm. C. The law of patents, Boston, Little, Brown, & Co., 3 vols., 1890.
Ross, E. A. Foundations of sociology, New York, Macmillan, 1905.
—— Social psychology, New York, Macmillan, 1908.
—— Principles of sociology, New York, Century, 1920.
Ruger, H. A. Psychology of efficiency, Archives of Psychology, No. 15, New York, Science Press, 1910.
Schwarz, O. L. General types of superior men, Boston, Gorham, 1916.
Smiles, S. Industrial biography, London, John Murray, 1884.
Smyth, W. H. Irascible Strong et al., New York, Knopf, 1926.
Sorokin, P. Social mobility, New York, Harper, 1927.
—— Contemporary, sociological theories, New York, Harper, 1928.
Spearman, C. E. The abilities of man, their nature and measurement, New York, Macmillan, 1927.
Souriau, P. Theorie de l'invention, Paris, Hachette, 1881.
Spencer, H. Social statics, New York, Appleton, 1896.
Stenquist, J. L. Measurements of mechanical ability, New York, Teachers College, 1923.
Stern, B. J. Social factors in medical progress, New York, Columbia Univ. Press, 1927.
Tarde, G. The laws of imitation, New York, Holt, 1903.
Taussig, F. W. Inventors and money makers, New York, Macmillan, 1915.
Temple, R. and C. Invention and discovery, London, Groombridge, & Sons, 1865.
Terman, L. M. Genetic studies of genius, 2 vols., Stanford, Stanford Univ. Press, 1926, 1927.
Tessier, C. O. The patent business, New York, Printing Dept., Salvation Army, 1921.
Thompson, E. P. How to make inventions, New York, Van Nostrand, 1893.

Thorndike, E. L. Educational psychology, vol. 1, New York, Teachers College, Columbia Univ., 1914.
Todd, A. J. Theories of social progress, New York, Macmillan, 1918.
Tozzer, A. M. Social origins and social continuities, New York, Macmillan, 1926.
Usher, A. P. A history of mechanical inventions, New York, McGraw-Hill, 1929.
Varendonck, J. The evolution of the conscious faculties, London, Allen & Uniom, 1923.
Vaughn, F. L. Economics of our patent system, New York, Macmillan, 1925.
Vaughn, W. F. The lure of superiority, New York, Holt, 1928.
Veblen, T. The instinct of workmanship, New York, Macmillan, 1914.
Vischer, S. S. Geography of American notables, Bloomington, Ind., Indiana Univ. Studies, No. 79, 1928.
Waite, J. B. Patent law, Princeton, Princeton Univ. Press, 1920.
Walker, A. H. Patents, New York, Baker, Voorhis, 2 vols., 1929, 6th edition.
Ward, L. F. The psychic factors of civilization, New York, Ginn, 1906.
—— Applied sociology, New York, Ginn, 1906.
—— Pure sociology, New York, Macmillan, 1907.
—— Dynamic sociology, New York, Appleton, 1917.
Warren, H. C. Elements of human psychology, Boston, Houghton Mifflin, 1922.
Watson, J. B. Psychology from the standpoint of a behaviorist, Phila., Lippincott, 1919.
Wile, F. W. A century of industrial progress, New York, Doubleday, 1928.
Wilkie, F. B. The great inventions, Phila., J. A. Ruth, 1883.
Williams, A. The romance of modern mechanism, London, Seeley Service & Co., 1912.
Wisehart, M. K. Marvels of Science, New York, Century, 1928.
Wood, J. G. Nature's teachings, London, J. S. Virtue & Co., 1883.
Woods, F. A. Mental and moral heredity in royalty, New York, Holt, 1906.
Woodworth, R. S. Dynamic psychology, New York, Columbia Univ. Press, 1918.
—— Psychology, New York, Holt, 1921.
Wright, M. Inventions and patents, New York, McGraw-Hill, 1927.
Yerkes, R. M. The new world of Science, New York, Century, 1920.
Young, K. Source book for social psychology, New York, Knopf, 1927.

Index of Names

INDEX OF SUBJECTS

Library of the Mystic Arts

A LIBRARY OF ANCIENT AND MODERN CLASSICS

APOCRYPHA, The. Intro. by Morton Enslin, Professor of Biblical Languages and Literature, St. Lawrence University. Size 7¼" x 11", xv + 239pp., bound in white and gold, 3-color slipcase. 62-12335. $15.00 REL

"A good book, like a virtuous woman, can be valued for a number of qualities. This makes its initial appeal through the beauty of its binding and printing. Only after one has admired these qualities does he read the familiar passages and move back to the excellent Introduction.

"In 1924 the Nonesuch edition of the Apocrypha appeared, limited to 1325 copies. This new edition is an almost exact facsimile of that very beautiful work, bound in a most attractive cover with stamped gilt design, and boxed. Most marked of its changes from the original, and one that enhances the value of the work considerably, is an Introduction by the editor of this Journal, Dr. Morton S. Enslin, who in brief, concise paragraphs provides excellent prefaces to the work as a whole and to each of the books individually. He places the Apocrypha in its proper context in biblical literature, indicates the inappropriateness of the name when applied to the books as a whole, and shows how it was that Luther split off these writings and placed them 'in the limbo between the Old Testament and the New.' The individual introductions serve to provide the backgrounds, probable datings, and general contents of each of the fourteen pieces. This is a valuable work for both the biblical scholar and the lover of fine books."—*J. Calvin Keene,* JOURNAL OF BIBLICAL LITERATURE

BIRREN, Faber. Color: A Survey in Words and Pictures: From Ancient Mysticism to Modern Science. index. 250 illus. 7⅝" x 10½", slipcased, 224pp. 62-18889. $15.00 PSYCH

In this marvelous encyclopedia of color facts and fancies, Faber Birren, leading consultant in America on the subject, offers a kaleidoscope of information for both the users of color in industry and science and the many who are intrigued by color artistically and psychologically. His contributions to the development of color application in government and industry have influenced us all. Here he offers the results of a lifetime devoted to his studies.

Illustrating his survey with more than two hundred and fifty illustrations in color, Mr. Birren conducts the reader on a leisurely stroll through primitive, ancient, medieval, and modern color conceptions, explaining color's mystic function, its many religious uses, the significance of gem stones, the relation of color to marriage and fertility.

A stimulating section on heraldry precedes an examination of color symbolism today. Color in medicine, from ancient cures to modern diagnoses, is dwelt upon at length, and medieval theories of alchemy are discussed.

The author includes an amusing account of the feud between Goethe and Sir Isaac Newton on color theory, and continues on to a consideration of modern spectroscopy and the wonders of human vision. The human aura is scrutinized, and the language of color, with charming and sometimes unexpected word derivations, dealt with extensively.

The relation of color to music, perhaps less well-known, is the subject of an unusual chapter, giving the history of color scales and color organs. In art, Renaissance artists, Impressionism, and Modern Painting are detailed with excellent illustrations.

CHANG, Garma C. C. Teachings of Tibetan Yoga. Introduction by John C. Wilson. 128pp. 62-22082. $5.00 YOGA

The author-translator who gave us the translation of *The Hundred Thousand Songs of Milarepa* now provides an introduction to the spiritual, mental, and physical exercises of his religion. Tibetan Yoga, or Tantrism, is summarized by the author in the following words: "The divinity of Buddahood is omnipresent, but the quickest way to realize this truth is to discover it within one's body-mind complex. By spiritual exercises and the application of Tantric techniques one can soon realize that his body, mind, and the 'objective world' are all manifestations of the divine Buddahood."

DINGWALL, Eric J. Some Human Oddities: Studies in the Queer, the Uncanny and the Fanatical. ill bibliog. 198pp. 62-14948 $6.00 PSYCH

DINGWALL, Eric J. Very Peculiar People: Portrait Studies in the Queer, the Abnormal and the Uncanny. ill. index. bibliog. 224pp. 62-14949. $6.00 PSYCH

"These reissues of two fascinating books, originally written in 1946 and 1951 respectively, will be welcomed by all the lovers of true tales of the weird, strange and abnormal. Here are stories, scholarly written and scientifically analyzed, of visionary mystics like Emanuel Swedenborg, masochistic saints like St. Mary Magdalene de Pazzi, flying friars like Joseph of Copertino, mediums *extraordinaires* like D. D. Home and Eusapia Palladino, pornographers de luxe like Hadrian Beverland, transvestites like James Allen, and many others."—M.D. PUBLICATIONS

"Dr. Dingwall recounts some real-life stories that rival fiction for strangeness. He views and interprets the lives of these queer folk through the eyes of a psychic researcher—one of great note, indeed, and one with a sound academic background. The author has combined his talents as historian, psychologist and psychic researcher to produce a work for the scholarly with a taste for the macabre."—MEDICAL JOURNAL OF AUSTRALIA

FLOURNOY, Theodore. From India to the Planet Mars; Intro. and final chapter by C. T. K. Chari. xxxvi+469 pages. 63-16228. $10.00 PSYCH

The passing years have served to confirm the eulogistic estimates of those best fitted to judge this work of the author, who was professor of psychology at the University of Geneva and died in 1921. F. W. H. Myers' *Human Personality* called Flournoy's book, "a model of fairness throughout." William McDougall's *Outline of Abnormal Psychology*, summed up the merits of the book: "Among the many cases of the trance-medium type, one stands out preeminent by reason of the richness and variety of the phenomena presented, of the thoroughness and competence with which it was studied, and of the success attending the endeavor to throw the light of science upon its complexities; I mean the case of Hélène Smith most admirably studied and reported by Th. Flournoy." William James praised it in equally high terms. Recent research into extra-sensory perception and the problems of survival and reincarnation has given a new and decisive importance to this classic. Flournoy's gift for narrative is unquestionable. One learns from him that a popular treatment is consistent with scientific carefulness.

The medium he studied became famous especially for two of her most convincing and most bizarre "incarnations." In the one she re-lived the life of a queen in 15th century India. In the other she was allegedly transported to Mars and described and drew pictures of its flora, fauna and intelligent beings, and wrote in the "Martian language."

Flournoy's critical studies of this medium demolished most of the claims made for her. But what he left standing is amazing enough. Some of what he left is now taken away by the new studies contributed to this volume by Professor Chari, a professor of philosophy and an eminent parapsychologist in India. Even he, however, must testify to the extraordinary verisimilitude of the medium's "memories" of 15th century India.

FOX, Oliver. Astral Projection: A Record of Out-of-the-Body Experiences. xiii+160 pages. 62-19195. $5.00 OCCULT

The noted psychic researcher, Dr. Hereward Carrington, reports in one of his works: "The only detailed, scientific and first-hand account of a series of conscious and voluntarily controlled astral projections which I have ever come across is that by Mr. Oliver Fox, published in the *Occult Review* for 1920." The articles were expanded into a book. This is its first publication in the United States.

The literature of psychic research includes many instances in which a person has an out-of-the-body experience. Sometimes it arises out of a very serious accident. Sometimes it comes in the course of a profound illness. At other times it results from the shock of tragic information or a harrowing experience. A considerable amount of material on out-of-the-body experiences is found in other books published by us: F. W. H. Myers' *Human Personality and its Survival of Bodily Death*, Mrs. Sidgwick's *Phantasms of the Living*, G. N. M. Tyrell's *Science & Psychical Phenomena & Apparitions*.

FRAXI, Pisanus (pseudonym of **ASHBEE, Henry Spencer).** 3 vols. Each indexed. v. 1. Index Liborum Phohibitorum. intro. by G. Legman. 51+lxxvi+543pp. v. 2. Centuria Liborum Absconditorum. lx+587pp. v. 3. Catena Liborum Tacendorum. lvii+591pp. All bound in buckram and boxed. 63-13985 $35.00 per set BIBLIOG

"The random bibliographical articles of which the present volumes are composed, sampling and describing at length the more difficult but elusive masterpieces of erotic literature in various languages" is the most important work of its kind in English. A 50-page introduction by G. Legman, whose name will be familiar to many librarians as a great bibliographer in his own right, makes clear the importance of this work, originally privately published a volume at a time (1877, 1879, 1885), of which this edition is a facsimile. "Henry Spencer Ashbee—to quote 'Pisanus Fraxi' by his real name—set out to do only a very limited thing, but in a thorough and profound way. He proposed simply to describe, and copiously to quote, some of the many hundreds of erotic books in various languages that had passed through his hands, and through the hands of some of his friends, during a long and assiduous career as a collector. His striking success, as opposed to the abysmal failure of most of his imitators, rises clearly from the limitations within which he was satisfied to work, without any megalomaniacal vaunting and flaunting of his interests and his evident erudition. Ashbee remains the principal guide-book and source work for the future moral historian of England and the 18th century, and has a great deal to tell any similar historian of England and the rest of Europe as well as America, to nearly the end of the 19th century as well."—*G. Legman*

GRILLOT DE GIVRY, Emile. Picture Museum of Sorcery, Magic and Alchemy. Introduction by Cynthia Magriel. 376 illus. index. 395pp. slipcased. 63-11177. $17.50 OCCULT

By common consent of students of these subjects, the best and most representative illustrations ever gathered in one volume are here. The text, excellently translated from the French, is equal to the illustrations. For the author is one of the great savants in this difficult and complex area of scholarship. Grillot De Givry (1874-1929), after a lifetime largely devoted to translating from Latin into French most of the famous hermetic texts, including Paracelsus, Savanarola, John Dee, Khunrath, Basilius Valentinus, gave the last years of his life to collecting this iconography of occultism.

HARRISON, Jane Ellen. Epilegomena to the Study of Greek Religion [and] Themis: a Study of the Social Origins of Greek Religion. 152 ills. index. lvi + 600 pp. 62-16379. $10.00 REL

"Jane Harrison (1850-1928) symbolizes the meeting between the more traditional classical studies and the disciplines of cultural anthropology and psychoanalytical psychology. She was a contemporary of Sir James Frazer, Sigmund Freud, and C. G. Jung and one of the first classical scholars to identify and discuss the *primitive* bases of the Greek religious tradition. It is largely under her influence that Olympian gods have come to be recognized as relatively late and predominantly literary figures, whereas she maintained the idea that it was the Mysteries, Dionysian and Orphic, that were the core of Greek religion. It is not surprising that the academic world has met her message with scepticism and hostility. In recent years, her books have become scarce on the market. The most recent reprint of "Themis" (1912) was in 1927, and the "Epilogemena" here reviewed is the reproduction of the one edition ever printed at Cambridge, England, in 1921. While she had numerous critics among her academic peers, she has also won the support and admiration of such great scholars as F. M. Cornford and Gilbert Murray, who contribute two long chapters to "Themis." The preface to the present edition, by John C. Wilson, and the "Jane Harrison Memorial Lecture," by Gilbert Murray, with which it concludes, are very helpful for an evaluation of her contribution to classical studies for the less well informed readers. Without taking sides on strictly scholarly issues, which are always open to revision and re-evaluation, one can claim the quality of greatness for Jane Harrison's writings and rejoice at their being made available to the reading public."—LIBRARY JOURNAL

"A book that changed my life—there are times when I think it is the most revolutionary book of the 20th century—has just been reissued, marking the 50th anniversary of its publication. It is *Themis*...Jane Harrison is truly what Edith Hamilton is popularly taken to be, the great lady who found Greece marble and left it living flesh."—*Stanley Edgar Hyman*
THE NEW LEADER

JAMES, William. The Varieties of Religious Experience; A Study in Human Nature; Enlarged Edition with Appendices and Introduction by Joseph Ratner. bibliog. index. 672pp. 63-14505. $10.00 REL

William James (1842-1910) began as a chemist and a physician. The physical side of medicine very soon ceased to interest him and he devoted his life to psychology and philosophy. Very early, too, he understood how shallow and unthinking was the attitude toward science of his colleagues at Harvard Medical School. He introduced Freud to his first American audience at a time when the medical profession anathematised psychoanalysis. He was the first to recognize the epochmaking importance of the discovery of the subliminal parts of the mind by F. W. H. Myers. He spent years studying the mediumship of Mrs. Piper and was the first American to become President of the Society for Psychical Research. He outraged the medical profession by becoming the principal spokesman in a successful fight to prevent requiring medical licenses of mental healers in Massachusetts. Finally, himself free of Christian belief or any other sectarian belief, he yet considered the cental task of his life to defend the legitimacy of religious belief. This is the great theme of this most fascinating and readable book.

James felt himself peculiarly fitted to explain mystics to non-mystics and vice versa and it is this successful role that makes this book a supreme triumph. The present edition of *Varieties* is notable for two things. James always meant to revise and expand it but never did. What Professor Joseph Ratner does now is to provide, in ten Appendices, about 100 pages of William James' other writings which bear on the central theme of *Varieties* and so, in effect, tell us the story of James' ideas on religion up to his death. Second, Professor Ratner provides a long Introduction which serves as a guide to those who may be perplexed by the various misleading interpretations of James foisted upon him during the 60 years since he wrote *Varieties*.

JUNOD, Henri A. The Life of a South African Tribe; 2 vols. intro. by Keith Irvine, Research Officer of the Ghana Mission. 150 ills. photos. index & glossary. 1230 pp. 62-18890. Slipcased. $20.00 AFRICA

"This is the first American edition of a classic anthropological study of an African tribe written by a Swiss missionary and first published in Europe as long ago as 1912 (this is the 1927 revised edition text.) Henri Junod came to what is now Mozambique in 1889, and lived for many years in the interior among the Bathonga people. On his return to Europe he wrote this monumental monograph, surprisingly enough in English when his own language was French. He died in 1934. Junod was inspired by a chance remark of the famed British historian, Lord Bryce, who regretted that no Roman has taken the trouble to investigate fully the ways of the Celtic people. Junod determined to perform this task for the Bathongas, who were still living in what might be described as their primeval state. The book examines in great detail their daily lives as individuals and as members of the tribe, their religion, culture, and social life. It is a massive and masterly performance, all the more valuable now since it represents a way of life that has virtually vanished. Half the Bathonga men now work in the South African mines, and civilization has profoundly affected their traditional customs. The two volumes are illustrated with photographs, maps and diagrams, and come boxed."—*John Barkham,* SATURDAY REVIEW SYNDICATE.

"The finest monograph on any African tribe."

—AFRICA, Journal of Anthropology.

KING, C. Daly. The States of Human Consciousness. approx. 256 pp. 63-10385. $7.50 PSYCH

Science, with all its promise, has diminished the old gods without providing aspirations worthy of twentieth century man. The aimlessness and frustration confronting us today has challenged philosophers to search deeply into the past, and into themselves, for a new approach to the human dilemma. From thinkers as far from us as ancient Egypt, or as near as the Gurdjieff Institute for the Harmonious Development of Man (founded in the 1920's), comes a clue to what we are seeking—a new dimension within man himself. There is an answer—to develop the human consciousness far beyond its present infantile state. In this profound book, the author uses the tools of science as steppingstones to go beyond science.

We know as normal today a Sleep state filled with restlessness and anxiety-ridden dreams; a Waking state of light hypnosis, phantasies and lack of awareness. Using the primary hypothesis of the Gurdjieff Institute, that man as a true individual is still only a potentiality, Dr. King analyzes the various neurological, physiological and psychological states of the organism to find the means whereby consciousness can be changed from a passive entity, capable only of blindly carrying out the body's orders, into an active 'I'-entity: a human "I" controlling every facet of his organism, and through this activity reaching an intimate awareness of the living universe.

Throughout history there have been moments when mankind was aware of abilities beyond those normally experienced. Gurdjieff is the first in modern times to attempt to create a rigorous discipline whereby man can enter states of higher consciousness at will and remain in them at length. The author was a student of Gurdjieff.

That there are different "degrees-of-being" of human beings will be a startling and even threatening idea to many. Yet—hence the great importance of this book—this may lead us to the answer to the human condition.

Dr. King is the author of *Beyond Behaviorism; The Psychology of Consciousness, Integrative Psychology* (with W. Mand G. H. Marston), among other books. He received his doctorate in Physiological Psychology at Yale University.

Roy Finch, Professor of Philosophy of Sarah Lawrence College, has written an Introduction on the life and work of Dr. King (who died while this book was in press); he has also placed this book in the context of Gurdjieff's work.

LEGMAN, G. The Horn book; studies in erotic bibliography and folklore. index. bibliog. approx. 500pp. $10.00 REF

The Journal of American Folklore, an academic periodical, published last year a special issue devoted to erotic folklore and obscenity. It may be too early to assess the significance of this landmark event, as a sign of America and its higher schools coming of age. Mr. Legman was the principal contributor to that issue of the Journal. Perhaps, then, one can say without irony that it marked the official discovery of Mr. Legman by that part of the academic world occupied with the same subjects to which our author has been contributing for the last twenty-five years. During those years, it has not been easy for Mr. Legman to find himself in print. He had to resort to Samuel Roth's periodical, American Aphrodite, where first appeared the title essay of the present book here expanded and revised. He published some six issues of his own periodical, Neurotica. He is perhaps best known for an essay he published in book form almost 15 years ago, Love and Death. With the exception of the Horn Book, which dates back in its original form to 1953, Mr. Legman has refused to permit us to reprint in this volume any of his work dating back more than a year or two. Except for the essay on Pisanus Fraxi and the three pieces from the Journal of American Folklore, this volume consists of new, unpublished material.

LELAND, Charles Godfrey. Gypsy Sorcery and Fortune Telling: Illustrated by Incantations, Specimens of Medical Magic, Anecdotes, Tales; intro. by Margery Silver. ill. index xxxiii+271pp. 62-22021. $10 ANTHROP

"First published in 1891, this delightfully esoteric work is the product of the prolific American author Leland, who did much of his research abroad where he founded the Gypsy Lore Society, and who, after some 20 years of study and travel, was able to claim, 'I have enjoyed gypsying more than any sport in the world.' And that is certainly the flavor of this reprinted volume which cites the gypsy as the carrier (*colporteur*) of constantly changing witchcraft legends, magic, and memories, as they swept across Europe and around the world from their earliest origins in southern Asia. The description of gypsy lore will charm its readers, much as the gypsy does—with good humor, tolerance, and no sense of patronizing airs (which so frequently spoil George Borrow and others)—in fact the charm may sometimes appear to obscure the authenticity of Leland's fine ethnological studies. Nevertheless, the book remains one of the most important records of the Romany people's passing beliefs. There are numerous drawings and diagrams, and an interesting new Introduction by Margery Silver, a free-lance writer on American history and literature. Recommended for all libraries that may have an interest in gypsy lore or the occult. Can there be any that do not?"—*Lee Ash,* LIBRARY JOURNAL

"The book is a rare treasure. Rich in knowledge, humor and feeling, it is highly recommended to those who would understand that mysterious tribe who sold good luck when they themselves had none."—*Per Sagereng,* SAN FRANCISCO NEWS—CALL BULLETIN.

LELAND, Charles Godfrey. Etruscan Magic and Occult Remedies; intro. by Margery Silver. index. ill. xxxiii + 385 pp. 63-18491. $10.00 ANTHROP

Etruscan is one of the lost languages. All that remains are a few inscriptions to which no one has yet found the linguistic key. True, archeologists have dug out many remains, especially their magnificent tombs, and we do have literary sources in the literature of the Romans who succeeded the Etruscans as rulers of the land, conquered and assimilated them. But all this is like reading Herodotus on ancient Egypt before we could understand the Egyptian language and use it to support Herodotus, modify him or correct him. In this impasse, the folklorist Leland (author of the gypsy study reviewed above) hit upon a simple but profound truth: that the peasantry of Tuscany, descended from the Etruscans, still preserved basic elements of the ancient Etruscan religion and culture. The Tuscan peasants had remained on the ancient lands, little touched in their rural isolation by the passing conquerors and centuries. They had eventually lost their language when Rome made them Roman citizens. But they had preserved their pagan beliefs. These peasants, of course, call themselves Catholics, but had succeeded in hiding from the priests their continued worship of the pagan deities of their ancestors. One can imagine with what astonishment Leland's first field work from Tuscany was greeted by the Congress of the Folklore Society in London in 1890; the news was reported in the next morning's *Times* as sensational. The original edition of this book, published soon after, was hailed by the serious cultural journals of the day as "a singular achievement" and "a unique accomplishment." Leland had seized his opportunity at a time when Tuscany's rural isolation made his findings of Etruscan remains relatively easy to prove. The clear implication of his work is that even when such remains are overlaid by later accretions they are still to be found. Despite the extraordinary importance of Leland's work and example, he has had few imitators. Jane Harrison (in *Epilegomena* and *Themis*, reviewed on page 8 of this catalogue) similarly marshaled anthropological field work among living peoples to throw new light on Greek religion. John Lawson followed even closer in Leland's footsteps by living among modern Greek peasants and finding there powerful survivals of ancient Greek religion (we shall shortly publish a new edition of his *Modern Greek Folklore and Ancient Greek Religion)*. But this method remains anathema to the philologist; the archeologists are neither equipped for it nor interested; and the anthropologists have not learned it. Scientifically, then, Leland's work remains almost as unique an achievement as it was 75 years ago.

Leland was not only a scientific innovator, but a delightful writer and gregarious literary companion. This book is as readable as any of his writings on the gypsies. In those the gypsies speak to us directly; so do the Tuscan peasants and their real priests, their witches and warlocks. In the first part, they tell us about their gods and goblins. In the second part, we are given their incantations, divination, medicine and amulets. The author himself supplied some 60 illustrations, his own drawings.

LOISY, Alfred. The Birth of the Christian Religion [and] The Origins of the New Testament. Intro. by W. Norman Pittenger, General Theological Seminary. index. xix + 768 pp. 62-18073. $10.00 REL

"English readers have not before had access to the writings of Alfred F. Loisy, one of the leaders of the "Catholic Modernism" which disturbed the Roman Catholic Church at the end of the 19th and the beginning of the 20th century. In this volume is presented the excellent translation of his last two books, "The Birth of the Christian Religion" and "The Origins of the New Testament". In them Loisy applies the critical standards regularly employed in the study of non-religious history to the New Testament and other writings of the period, since he believed that unless the faith of men could survive the closest and most rigorous scrutiny by the scientific apparatus available to scholars, men of integrity and honesty could not hold that faith. His own Church excommunicated him for the radical conclusions of his study, and even to readers of this generation Loisy's conclusions are more than a little startling, but the religious spirit with which they are written conveys Loisy's own belief that true religion can always survive the inaccuracies and distortions of the historical record. 'What matters', he wrote, 'is the fire they (the men of the New Testament) kindled, and it is a fire that will never die till mankind is no more.' Students of the development of Christianity and the Church cannot afford to miss this striking and moving contribution to the study in which the last word has by no means been said."—VIRGINIA KIRKUS SERVICE.